To The Moon

A MULTICULTURAL ASSEMBLY BOOK

Written by
TIM HUGHES

Illustrated by
ELLEN, MICHAEL AND FIONA HUGHES

First Published
January 05 in Great Britain by

PUBLISHING

The moral right of the author has been asserted in accordance with the
Copyright, Designs and Patents Act 1988

A CIP record for this work is available from the British Library

ISBN 10: 1-904904-20-3
ISBN 13: 978-1-904904-20-5

Typeset by Educational Printing Services Limited

Educational Printing Services Limited
Unit 6, Glenfield Park 2, Northrop Avenue, Blackburn BB1 5QH
Telephone: (01254) 686500   Fax: (01254) 686501
E-mail: enquiries@eprint.co.uk   Website: www.eprint.co.uk

Contents

Contents

To The Moon

This multicultural assembly book will take the children on a journey around the world.

It contains forty stories, each with a different background and theme.

Some of the stories are written in the style of Folk Tales, others feature day-to-day events in various cultural settings.

Many of the characters face a conflict or challenge, which they have to overcome.

There are touches of magic and moments of happiness and sadness.

A number of the stories are based on real events.

Each story is provided with a Thought/Prayer.

There are a number of illustrations, which may be copied and projected to assist the story telling.

The material may be photocopied and used in classrooms for literacy, history, R.E. etc.

> **Theme:** Anger
>
> **Introduction:**
> *This story is set in a school in New York. It deals with a young student who finds it hard to control his temper. He is often the target of provocation, but he has to learn some new strategies for anger management.*

Toby was angry. He was often angry. Sometimes very angry.

It didn't take much to get him worked up.

Justin, who was in his class, knew this and he would use it to good effect.

"Loser," Justin whispered after Toby answered incorrectly.

Toby jumped up and dashed towards Justin, fists clenched, teeth tight and fire in his chest.

"Toby, sit down at once!" cried Mr Newman, as he stepped promptly across to the incident.

It was all Toby could do to control himself and not let fly with a punch to wipe that smug smile off Justin's face.

Toby looked at his teacher through watery eyes. He felt like crying and swearing all at once but did neither and returned to his desk.

Toby's school was in New York in The United States of America. It was a large school. A good school with fine teachers and many eager students. Toby really liked it, but he was getting in to more and more trouble because of his temper and that blistering anger inside him which was so ready to erupt.

The thing was, there was nobody he could talk to about his feelings. His mum was under pressure. Dad wasn't there any more, Toby only saw him during the long vacation and Pete, his big brother, was working in Washington now and only came home to collect things or have a meal.

Down in the gym the boys were playing indoor baseball. Toby saw Justin across the room. The throb of annoyance started to well up. Justin was bound to say something. Perhaps Toby should get in there first. But no, he was invited to bat and his attention and energies were soon put into the game.

His team won and they all squatted in the corner sharing a coke, laughing about the result.

Toby didn't notice Justin come up behind him and wasn't prepared for the shove in the back that Justin delivered with significant force. Toby fell sprawling on the wooden floor. Justin cackled and in a sarcastic voice said, "At least you can hit a ball, Dopey Toby, pity you can't hit a good score in maths."

A pain shot through Toby's head and blurred his vision. Not a pain from the blow but from the power of the anger. Toby bounced up and grabbed Justin by the collar, pushed him back against the wall bars and lifted his hand to strike him. The rest of his team reacted swiftly and intervened, grabbing Toby by the shoulders, shouting at Justin for his provocation. Mr Newman had witnessed the scene from the door. He walked briskly across.

"Toby, report to my office during afternoon recess. I'm not going to tolerate any more of your outbursts," the teacher announced with authority and a hint of exasperation.

Toby shook himself free from his team mates, looked at them accusingly but could not make eye contact with his enemy, Justin. He stormed from the gym and went to find a solitary corner.

He waited outside Mr Newman's office, impatiently rocking from one foot to the other. The door opened and Mr Newman beckoned the guilty boy inside.

"Sit down Toby," the teacher's voice was gentle. Toby appreciated this and felt a little more secure. "Toby, nearly every day you lose your temper with somebody. Justin Skinner seems to be your latest target," Mr Newman confirmed.

"But Sir, he's winding me up. Always having a go. I just can't stop myself when he starts," insisted Toby, his temperature rising again.

"It's no good Toby, you've got to get some self control. This could end in you being expelled," the teacher continued, "there are a few tricks for anger that might help."

Mr Newman moved across to the whiteboard, picked up a pen and wrote the numbers one to five in a vertical column.

"Here we go," thought Toby, "the count to ten and take deep breaths speech."

Mr Newman lifted the pen and said, "When you feel like you're going to lose your temper and hit Justin, try these. Number one. Say excuse me." Mr Newman wrote the words 'excuse me' in capitals on the board. "Number two. Breathe slowly through your nose and number three, turn and walk away."

'I knew it,' thought Toby.

"Number four," continued the teacher, "as you're walking begin counting and do not stop walking or counting until you reach twenty five."

Toby rolled his eyes and wished he could leave.

"And here's the real trick," Mr Newman enthused, "as you're walking imagine Principal Johnson sitting behind his desk wearing a pink ballet dress and a diamond tiara."

Toby looked up at his teacher not sure whether he had heard him correctly. A smile spread across the man's face.

"Yes that's right, imagine your headteacher in a ballet dress. That will soon make you smile and distract you from Justin Skinner's taunts."

Toby laughed out loud. It was good to laugh, he hadn't done that for a long time. "Oh Sir. I'll try it. And I will try not to lose it," Toby assured this kind man.

Toby politely said goodbye and closed the door behind him.

It was only a day later when Justin tried to wind him up again.

"Second hand trainers today Toby," smirked Justin in the cloakroom.

A flush of fury swept across Toby. He stood square up to Justin. And then he remembered.

"Excuse me, I've got to go," Toby coughed.

He breathed deeply, turned and walked out towards the corridor. He began the slow count, whispering under his breath. A picture started to form in his mind. He saw the usually serious headmaster stand up from his large oak desk. He was wearing a voluminous pink dress and dainty ballet shoes. The music started in Toby's mind and in his daydream Principal Johnson began singing, arms stretched out, smiling mouth wide open. "Tomorrow, Tomorrow, I love you Tomorrow. You're only a day away," sang the principal.

The image faded and Toby found himself at the other end of the corridor, leaning against the wall. Laughing with real gusto.

"Glad to see you're enjoying yourself Toby," said Mr Newman as he walked past.

The anger was gone.

Thought/Prayer

God of the World,

At some time or other everyone feels angry. It is quite natural. Sometimes we are angry because something has happened to annoy us. At other times we can lose our temper easily because we are not happy with some things in our lives.

May we think deeply about our anger and learn to control our strong feelings. May we use our emotions and energy to make the world around us a more peaceful place.

These are our thoughts and this is our prayer.

Michael Such and the Cake Shop

> **Theme:** Doing the Right Thing
>
> **Introduction:**
> *It is often not easy to do the right thing, to make the correct choice. This story is about two young friends who are tempted to take advantage of a situation when they know it is not the right thing to do.*

The bell rang and Mrs Powell asked the children to stand for the prayer.

"Enjoy your lunchtime and be good," she called as the class tumbled out to meet the dinner ladies.

Michael and Ted made haste out of the side gate. They were among a handful of children who went home for lunch.

"I'm so hungry," groaned Michael, "let's go to the cake shop." Ted looked sheepish and responded, "I've got no money."

"Don't worry," Michael boomed, "I'm loaded!"

The two mates pressed their noses to the cake shop window. Their tummies jumped with hunger and anticipation of a delicious bun.

"I'd like a cream finger," proclaimed Ted hopefully.

"Custard tart for me," smiled Michael. The boys dived into the shop with Michael rattling coins in his pocket.

A young and pretty assistant, who the boys didn't recognise, leant over the counter.

"A custard tart and a cream finger please," said Michael politely.

The assistant moved carefully and placed the cakes in separate bags.

"Eighty two pence please," she said, placing the bags on the glass counter.

"Oh eighty two, I haven't got that much." Michael hesitated and then continued, "Maybe we'll have two pieces of bread and butter pudding instead."

Both boys sighed with disappointment. The shop assistant looked around and then pushed the bags containing the custard tart and cream finger forward towards the boys.

"Have them," she offered, "free. Go on you can have them."

Michael and Ted timidly reached forward and lifted the bags.

"For free?" questioned Michael.

The young lady smiled and nodded.

Both boys were not sure. This couldn't be right. But the temptation was too great.

"Thanks," the boys cheered and skipped out.

The happy lads laughed and coughed as they jogged along the high street eating their free food.

After lunch, when they went back to the playground, the two friends excitedly told their classmates about the cakes. Although both Michael and Ted were pleased they had the hint of a guilty feeling.

The next day, however, any guilty emotions were pushed away by the familiar lunchtime hunger.

Cautiously they crossed the threshold of the cake shop. They were thrilled to see the happy face of the shop assistant. Before the boys could say a word the lady pronounced, "A custard tart and a cream finger." She placed them in bags. "There you are lads, enjoy them!" she continued confidently.

This time the two boys looked around uncertainly then grabbed the bags and backed out of the door whispering their thanks.

They paused before they took a bite and then sunk their teeth into the sweet pastries.

"Cakes for free again," Ted spluttered.

"Yeah," Michael said as he swallowed down the last of his custard tart.

"But why is she giving us cakes?" questioned Ted.

"I don't know and I don't care," replied Michael, although it was clear from his voice that he did feel uneasy.

At noon the next day both boys were quite quiet as they left the school site. Ted looked at Michael with a question in his eyes.

"Yes let's," roared Michael.

There was a crazy confidence about the boys as they jumped into the shop.

"Cakes please," shouted Ted cheekily.

"Free cakes please," echoed his friend. But as their eyes met the eyes of the young assistant they saw distress in her look. Standing behind her was an older, stern looking lady. She was obviously the manager.

"What do you mean?" The manager said curtly, "what do you mean free cakes?"

Nobody knew what to say. Michael and Ted felt a wave of embarrassment flow through them. Nothing they could do would hide their shame or save their young benefactor from the consequences.

"If you've been giving these boys cakes, you'll have to pay for them," pronounced the manager standing uncomfortably close to her young employee. She then turned to the boys. "And do you want cakes?" she interrogated Michael and Ted.

"Er no thank you, I haven't any money," murmured Michael.

"Well you'd better go then there's nothing for free here," spat the manager.

The boys turned and walked out of the shop. Once outside they bolted along the street in a panic. When they reached a bench they sat down and looked at one another. Michael thought he should laugh to prove that he didn't care but he didn't feel like laughing. Ted wanted to curse the manager but decided not to.

"We shouldn't have had those cakes," declared Michael.

"No," agreed Ted, "I bet she'll be in trouble."

They moved off the bench and went home for their midday meal and although they should have been hungry they found they could eat very little.

Thought/Prayer

God of The World,

May we have the strength and the wisdom to do the right thing. Often we are faced with a choice and even though we may know which is the correct option we are tempted to go with a decision that benefits us at the expense of others.

May we use our experience and understanding to follow a sensible course of action.

These are our thoughts and this is our prayer.

An illustration for this story is to be found on page 135.

An illustration for this story is to be found on page 135.

11th February 1990

> **Theme:** The Release of Nelson Mandela
>
> **Introduction:**
> *On 11th February 1990 the world was waiting for the release of one of the most important leaders of modern times.*

Annie was there in South Africa outside the prison. She saw him appear.

It was so, so hot and Annie's feet were tired. She blinked out the sweat that had trickled uncomfortably from her forehead into her eyes. She stood on her toes again. She craned her neck attempting to see above the crowd. The waiting was unbearable but the excitement and pent up joy was like a feast of emotions.

The huge crowd was calm, everyone could sense that the shared passion of liberation was about to heal so many scars.

Annie looked again, straining her gaze towards the gates, the world at last would see the face of Nelson Mandela. As she contemplated his arrival she clutched the pendant that she wore around her neck. Her mother had given this to her a few months before she had died. Inside the pendant was a picture of her father. He had died when Annie was only three. Oh, how her mother and father would have enjoyed today. How they would have celebrated the glory of Nelson's release. All their efforts, the years of determination and fighting would have been realised today. Annie let her head drop, she coughed, wiped a trickle from her cheek and turned to her Auntie Mary.

"Mary, Momma would have been happy today," she offered.

"Oh darling, your momma would have been twitching and dancing," her aunt smiled. "We all wish she were here. But you know Annie, I feel that she is."
Annie laughed and wrapped both of her hands around the fattest part of Mary's arm.

A hiss and then a low throb hummed from deep within the crowd. Everyone went back on tiptoes looking towards the gates of the prison. The gates of Victor-Verster Prison shook with potential. It was a full hour after the published time.

"He must come soon," called Annie, "Come on Nelson, come on Nelson."

As if responding to her plea the gates rattled open.

Flanked by all manner of people, some in uniform, some in suits, came a couple. A handsome smiling African man with greying hair. A pretty round faced younger woman with a colourful scarf adorning her head.

"Nelson Mandela, Nelson Mandela," the earth shook with the chanting of his name.

He stepped forward. He was smart and composed in his brown suit and tie. He smiled at the ecstatic crowds and then lifted his arm and punched the air in triumph.

It was a signal to everybody. To Annie and Mary, to the people of South Africa. To the whole world.

He was free and the march to freedom for the people of South Africa was more real than ever.

Nelson Mandela's smile shone like the most magical sunburst across the crowd. He then moved to a smart silver car and climbing in, he began waving to everyone lining the roads.

Annie turned to her aunt. Her face was aching with the power of her smiles and laughter. She saw that Mary was crying. Deep, deep sobs shaking her whole body.

"Mary, Mary," Annie called.

"Oh my darling, Oh my darling, I've waited so long for this moment."

With that Mary gathered up her skinny niece in her powerful arms. She hugged her tight and continued to laugh and cry rocking her from side to side.

All around people were singing, dancing, thanking God and cheering.

Some boys were running after Nelson's procession of cars that was heading for Cape Town.

"11th of February 1990, I will never forget this day Mary," Annie declared and with that the two sat down exhausted.

Thought/Prayer

God of Freedom and Justice,

We are grateful for the bravery and determination of the men and women who have brought about peace, justice and equality in the world.

May we follow their example in our daily lives.

These are our thoughts and this is our prayer.

Captain McCullough

Theme: Greed

Introduction:
When a Scottish Fisherman has a run of poor catches he is tempted by his greed to act unwisely.

Biting wind blew against the cheeks of the fisherman. It was very early in the morning when Captain McCullough and his crew pushed off from the jetty. A few dots of light flickered around the Scottish town; all was very quiet.

Captain McCullough looked out towards the dark horizon, he had a determined but worried look in his eyes. He had taken his small fishing trawler out to sea for the last three days and although he and the crew had worked hard they had caught no fish and the boat had returned empty.

"Don't worry Captain," said Jamesey, the first mate, "I'm sure we'll have a good catch today."

"I hope so Jamesey," replied the captain, "we can't afford to return to port with an empty boat tonight."

The small craft bobbed on the choppy sea. The sun was rising. A mist, which had lingered was quickly blown away by the cold wind. Captain McCullough grasped the lever and shut off the main engine.

"Right lads, get out the nets," he called.

Suddenly all the fishermen scurried about heaving the heavy net over board. Once the net was in the water the captain powered up the boat and it started moving slowly, dragging the net.

After half an hour the captain gave the order for the net to be pulled up. As the men struggled with the net, slowly dragging it aboard, Captain McCullough felt nervous – would there be a catch today?

The net slumped on the deck, a single fish flipped its fin pathetically.

"I'm sorry Captain," consoled Jamesey, "it's poor water again."

The captain strode back into the small wheelhouse cabin and slammed the door.

Jamesey turned the boat and looked towards the direction of the port.

After twenty minutes of chugging through the water the captain suddenly burst out of the cabin.

"Look," he called, "look over there, the gulls must have found a shoal."

Half a mile away a flock of seagulls was wheeling around above the waves. Their screeching carried through the air. As the trawler approached, the men could clearly see the swell of the fish. Thousands of silver bodies glistened near the surface. The fishermen had rarely seen such a huge amount of fish.

Captain McCullough laughed out loud.

"The nets lads," he bellowed and he himself took hold of the ropes and flung the nets into the water. No doubt this time – the nets were soon filled with a writhing mass of fish, the boat was clearly forced across by the pressure.

Every muscle of every person on the boat strained as they dragged the loaded net up into the boat.

"It's fantastic, fantastic lads," cried the captain.

Hundreds of large fish slapped out onto the deck, the men immediately started pushing them into boxes, and storage areas.

Captain McCullough looked over the side – and saw that the shoal was still just as large.

"The nets, Jamesey are they ready?" he called. Jamesey leant over the side of the boat and peered down at the swirling fish.

"Captain," he answered, "these are all yearlings, too small for our nets."

"Jamesey," retorted the captain, "take out the small grade nets."

"But Captain, we're not supposed to use the small grade at this time of year, the fish stocks . . ."

"Do as you are told Jamesey," shouted the captain angrily, stepping forward towards his first mate.

"And Captain," continued Jamesey uneasily, "the boat is full, this is a great catch, we've no room for more."

"The small grade nets!" bellowed the captain.

Dutifully Jamesey and the other sailors lifted the small grade nets from their boxes and dropped them overboard. Everyone looked uncertain except Captain McCullough who eyed the bubbling shoal greedily.

Once again another massive catch was loaded on the deck. Jamesey felt the craft strain with the weight.

"Right back to port lads," called the captain.

The motors laboured as the heavy boat fought its way thought the waves. A wind whipped up and the waves grew larger. The spray of the sea flashed across the deck.

"Captain we're too low in the water for these waves. The boat is overloaded," Jamesey pleaded.

"We'll make it Jamesey, just steer the boat."

Before the words had hardly left his mouth, a larger wave crashed over the deck and caught the captain knocking him off balance. He was suddenly dragged backward by another incoming wave and thrown overboard. He flapped and splashed in the water. His cries were merely gurgles as his head disappeared under the dangerous waves.

The boat had moved away from the captain and even though he tried, Jamesey found it hard to turn the vessel as it was so heavy with fish.

Jamesey knew that if he didn't act quickly the captain would be lost forever. Quickly he pulled the deck release lever and a flap in the side of the boat opened and the fish that were on the deck slid flapping and slithering into the water. Suddenly the boat felt lighter and Jamesey pulled the wheel around directing the craft towards the captain.

A rope and buoyancy aid was thrown to the captain who grabbed at it. He was pulled aboard and crashed, gasping for air on the wet deck.

"Right," shouted Jamesey, "let's get back."

It took two hours for the ship to make its way to shore. The captain was taken to the hospital and Jamesey and the crew packed the catch of fish into ice crates for market.

The next morning Jamesey walked into the hospital to find the captain sitting up in bed. The captain looked embarrassed.

"I should never have cast the small nets Jamesey, I was greedy," he said softly with a guilty sounding voice. He continued talking, a croak sounding in his voice. "You saved my life Jamesey, thank you, I shall always be in your debt."

"Don't say another word Captain," replied Jamesey, "you're safe and we caught a load of fish, that's enough now."

He smiled, shook the captain's hand, and walked out of the hospital and back to the port.

Thought/Prayer

God of the Deep Oceans and High Mountains,

We are grateful for all that we have. Sometimes we are tempted by our greed to want more. This may cause us to do something that is not right.

May we be satisfied with our lives and not allow our greed to make us act unwisely.

We think especially of the children and adults who live with poverty and starvation.

May the good influence of kind people help to provide a better quality of life for the needy and disadvantaged.

These are our thoughts and this is our prayer.

An illustration for this story is to be found on page 136.

Building Bridges

Theme: Making Friends

Introduction:
The two boys in this story enjoy playing in a small stream behind their houses. They are strangers, but a challenge prompts them to work together. It also brings about a new friendship.

Shamraz liked his house. He had his own bedroom. The garden was big enough to play cricket with his brother and it was close to the shop where he bought his crisps.

Best of all, however, was the stream behind the gardens where he could play. The water wasn't deep and although there was quite a lot of litter, it was a quiet and wonderful place.

Shamraz had a project. It was to build a really strong bridge across the stream. He had been gathering planks of wood, crates and string. He had attempted various designs but none of them were strong enough to take his weight. Eventually all of the bridges had collapsed and floated down the stream in bits.

One clear morning in June, Shamraz had gone down to the stream to begin another bridge build when he saw some wood, large cans and tyres further up the stream. Shamraz ignored the new equipment and set about his latest design.

Shamraz was interrupted by the arrival of another boy who was moving towards the pile of junk. The boy was about the same age as Shamraz. He had blonde hair and scruffy clothes. He had approached the stream from the other side. Perhaps he lived in the house on the other side, thought Shamraz.

The boy immediately became busy with his equipment. Shamraz noticed he had a hammer and nails. He was trying to nail a large plank to a wooden crate. He was bridge building too. Shamraz felt a little uncomfortable and tried not to look over at the boy.

Both lads laboured for more than an hour. Eventually Shamraz had finished his latest design. The wood was secured with rope and the plastic crate was weighed down with bricks. The bridge looked strong and secure.

Shamraz stepped on.

The structure wobbled slightly but held his weight. He moved cautiously to the centre.

Suddenly there was a creak and the plank twisted, overturned the crate and sent Shamraz flailing into the water on his hands and knees.

Shamraz cursed.

The other boy looked up alarmed by the noise. Shamraz stepped out of the stream shaking his legs trying to disperse as much water as possible. He kicked his failed bridge and sat down in the grass.

The other bridge builder had completed his construction and was ready for the first crossing. Like Shamraz, the other boy stepped on nervously. He took a few tentative steps before disaster struck. The nails were ripped out of the wood and the whole structure broke beneath its engineer. He too cursed and then turned and marched away towards his house in disgust.

The next day was another fine and hot new morning. Shamraz was up and out early. When he arrived at the stream he found the boy looking down at his pieces of bridge. The two boys stood gazing at each other across the water.

"Want to try again?" asked the boy.

"Build a bridge?" Shamraz replied with a question.

"Yeah, I'll get my wood," the boy shouted, running along the bank, "I'm Peter," he shouted over his shoulder.

Peter soon returned, his arms struggling to carry the assortment of planks, large tin cans and tools.

The two boys soon set to work. They discussed their ideas and made suggestions to each other about the way to construct the bridge. They found that both had good ideas. Peter was accurate with his nails, whilst Shamraz was able to twist and tie the ropes so that the joins were strong.

After labouring for nearly two hours the bridge was complete. Shamraz felt confident. Peter looked satisfied. They stood at either side of the bridge.

"Where are you from?" Peter enquired.

"The house over there," said Shamraz pointing to his house between the lilac trees. "My mum and dad have lived there since I was born. They came from Pakistan," he continued.

"I've seen you playing here a few times," Peter offered.

"Well let's try it then," suggested Shamraz. He placed his foot on the bridge. It was firm. The other foot was brought forward until he stood in the centre of the structure. It was sound. Shamraz held out his hand to Peter. Peter moved forward. Both boys were waiting for the collapse. The bridge held strong. It shook a little but was solid.

"Yes," declared Peter, "it's good!"

Soon the two boys were running to and fro across the bridge jumping off to the bank now and then.

"Come up to my house," said Peter after a while. "I've got more tools in the shed, maybe we can build a den."

Shamraz smiled and followed his new friend up to the back gate of a nearby house. In the garden a man was cleaning a lawnmower. He looked up at the boys. He stood up when he saw Shamraz. His expression was a little puzzled looking.

"Hello," he said half smiling.

"This is Shamraz, Dad, we've built a bridge between our houses," Peter declared happily.

"Good, nice to meet you Shamraz," announced Peter's dad. "Bridge builders between homes, good idea lads," he confirmed.

The boys laughed and delved into the shed looking for more equipment.

Thought/Prayer

God of Friendship,

We have many opportunities in our lives to build bridges, to make friends. Although we are different from one another, we are the same in so many ways; the things that we enjoy, our feelings and our hopes for the future.

May we cherish our friendships, respect our friends and enjoy our time together.

May we also grasp any chance to build a bridge between different people.

These are our thoughts and this is our prayer.

Theme: Extinct and Endangered Animals

Introduction:
This story, set in the Indian Ocean over three hundred years ago, imagines that a colony of Dodos survived extinction thanks to one determined bird.

340 years ago on a small and beautiful island in the middle of the Indian Ocean lived a colony of birds. These birds were large like geese. They had small stubby wings and unusual looking curly beaks. They were flightless, they could not fly. They would wander happily at the shore line on the soft sand and push their beaks into the warm water seeking out shrimps and crabs to eat. These birds were called dodos.

The dodos had no enemies, no worries, they did not know any dangers. So unlike many birds they were not nervous or afraid.

They had many friends, the monkeys that played in the nearby trees who would laugh at their unusual appearance and the seagulls who would swoop down on to the shore and tell the dodos about the amazing things they had seen.

Amongst the group of dodos there was one particular dodo who was a little different from the rest. His name was Bertol. He was worried. He had heard the seagulls talk about the large ships they had seen carrying humans to all parts of The Indian Ocean. He had bad dreams. He wondered what would happen if the humans visited their peaceful island. He felt the humans would bring trouble. Often Bertol would talk to the other dodos about his fear of humans. But the dodos ignored him and thought he was a little strange.

One fine spring morning a large black backed gull named Cara wheeled on to the shore screeching, "Ships are coming, humans in ships are heading this way!"

Many dodos picked their heads out of the sandy water and looked up to the horizon. Sure enough two large sailing ships were heading determinedly towards the island.

The dodos were excited as happy looking sailors came splashing ashore. Bertol however stood back from the water and told his family to keep away from the visitors.

To the men from the ships the dodos were indeed an unusual sight. They looked like large chickens and the sailors were amazed when many dodos came up close to them out of curiosity.

But Bertol was unhappy. He didn't like the look of the swords that the men carried. He felt frightened when the sailors built big fires on the beach.

And then suddenly his worst fears came true. The visiting sailors started to chase some of the largest dodos along the beach. Bertol saw the sailors waving their swords above their heads. The dodos were slow moving and of course could not fly away. Bertol couldn't watch as he heard the frightened screech of his friends as the men began killing them for food.

Bertol was short of breath. Quickly he gathered his family together and whispered, "We must leave, we can't stay here. I can see it. We are not safe."

Dragging the youngest birds behind them, Bertol's family rushed as quickly as their short legs could carry them through the trees to the other side of the island.

"Where are you going in such a hurry?" laughed the monkeys.

But Bertol did not answer. "Keep moving, don't stop," he shouted to the dodos following.

The next morning Bertol and his family woke up still tired, shaken and weary, on the far side of the island. Was that a bad dream, wondered Bertol. But before he could answer his own question, Cara the large gull flapped down on to the beach.

"Bertol, Bertol, you'll never believe what happened. Those men that came on the ships started chasing the dodos and . . ."

Cara did not finish her sentence, but looked frightened.

"I know," replied Bertol, "I saw it, we must leave this island."

"How can we leave?" questioned another smaller dodo, "we can't fly, we can't swim, we're trapped."

The young dodos began to cry. Bertol gazed out at the waves, what did the future hold for dodos, he mused.

Cara shot down to the beach again. "Another boat, another boat," she cried.

A small rowing boat floated in to view. It bobbed on the swell, there was no sign of life, it appeared empty.

"There are no humans in it," confirmed Cara.

Bertol fluttered forwards to the sea edge and examined the wooden boat. "This is it," he called, " we can escape in this."

The other dodos looked at him bewildered, they had always thought Bertol a little strange, now they were sure he was completely crazy.

"Look," he continued, "if we stay here the humans will kill us too, they'll find us and destroy us, until there are no dodos left."

"It's true," confirmed Cara, "I've seen what the humans have done, they have nearly wiped out all the other dodos."

After a little more flapping of stubby wings and waving of beaks the remaining group of dodos clambered awkwardly into the boat. They waited for the tide to catch the vessel and then found themselves drifting away from the island that had been the home of the dodo since time began.

They sailed for several days. Eventually another smaller island came in to view. Cara wheeled above them and confirmed that the island was deserted.

"No humans at all, I promise," she called down to them.

The boat scratched on to the shore and the group of frightened dodos tripped out on to the sand. They cautiously looked around, nervous that they may meet enemies.

After a short while Bertol announced, "I think it's safe, there are no humans here."

Over the next few days the surviving dodos got used to their new surroundings. They found food and safe places to roost and nest.

Days turned in to months. Each week Cara the seagull would visit bringing news from their old island. On one occasion she looked very serious. She landed and hung her head, a tear dropped from her eye.

"They're all gone," she declared. "There are no more dodos, the last few were hunted and killed. They are saying that the dodo is extinct."

Bertol pondered for a moment, grieving. And then said, "We can never let humans find us, the only way we can survive is by being completely secret."

In the years that followed eggs were laid and hatched, baby dodos stumbled around learning to walk and feed. It wasn't long before Bertol was a grandfather and then a great grandfather.

In the late afternoon he would often tell generations of dodos the story of how they had escaped the humans and fled to the safety of their new island home.

"But Great Grandfather," asked one small dodo, "won't the humans come to this island one day?"

"No my dear, the humans don't even know this island exists. My good friends the seagulls tell me that the humans have no knowledge of our small island, so we are safe."

"But Great Grandfather why did the humans kill off all the other dodos, why would they want to do that?" continued the young bird.

"I have no idea," replied Bertol, "but I hope that it never happens again. Humans think that dodos are extinct, perhaps one day they will miss us."

"I hope so," squeaked the little dodo and she walked in to the warm sea water on a far off island hidden somewhere in the Indian Ocean.

And there the dodos remain secret but alive forever.

Thought/Prayer

God of the World,

So many species of animals and plants have become extinct because of the damage done by humans.

May we respect all creation and not allow any species to be destroyed because of our lifestyle and greed.

We are grateful for the work of conservation groups who try hard to preserve endangered animals.

These are our thoughts and this is our prayer.

An illustration for this story can be found on page 137.

> **Theme:** Eid
>
> **Introduction:**
> *This story describes a family preparing for Eid. Their favourite pet is missing and Kasim is doing his best to help.*

It was the day before Eid and everyone in Kasim's house was very busy. Kasim was doing his best to keep out of the way. His dad had been out late driving his taxi and was tired. The whole family were up early to eat breakfast before it was light. It was hard fasting and Kasim knew that later that day he would be having those familiar twinges of hunger bubbling in his tummy.

Everyone sat in silence eating. Mrs Ahmed, Kasim's mum came bursting into the kitchen. She wasn't happy Kasim could tell, her top lip was straight, her shoulders were held tight. Finally she spoke crossly.

"This house is a mess, the food is not ready for tomorrow, the washing is piling up and you are all sitting there eating!"

Before any of them had a chance to speak she continued, pointing at Kasim. "You said you would clean up your bedroom Kasim. Your cricket kit is all over the floor, your cards are scattered all round the place and your bag is not ready for school."

Kasim, his brother Mohi and his dad hastily cleaned the table and shuffled out of the kitchen.

"And has anyone seen Twinkle?" Mrs Ahmed said with sadness in her voice, "I haven't seen her for days."

Twinkle was the family cat, well she was Mrs Ahmed's cat. She had owned Twinkle since before she was married. It was obvious that Mrs Ahmed was worried and upset about her pet.

Kasim pulled on his school uniform and then tried to put his bedroom in order. He kicked his cricket bat under the bed and tried to hide the dirty socks under his pillow.

As he was leaving for school his mum called from the kitchen. Kasim could hear the crashing of plates and dishes.

He tentatively went in.

"Kasim you come straight home today. No cricket on the field. I need help. It's Eid tomorrow, your uncle will be here and there's lots to do."

Kasim nodded and slumped out.

"Oh no," he thought, "no cricket." Well at least it was Eid tomorrow. A day off school and all of that lovely food and perhaps a new cricket bat from his uncle. Kasim loved it when Uncle Aqib came. They had fantastic games of cricket together. Kasim always boasted that his uncle had played for the county team when he was younger.

When school was finished Kasim ran home. He was famished, but he knew the hungry feeling in his stomach was worth it. He was proud of his fast for Ramadan. And tomorrow was Eid.

As he approached the house he thought he would quickly nip into the garage to find his cricket stumps. He would get them out ready for a game with his uncle. Kasim pulled the garage door, it creaked, it was always stiff and hard to open. After a good deal of tugging and panting Kasim managed to prise open the door. He went in and quickly slammed it shut behind him.

The atmosphere in the garage was unusual. It was a combination of smells. The oily paint smell, the scent of foxes, the hint of grass cuttings. It was dark too and strangely quiet.

Kasim rummaged in amongst the rakes, spades and sticks in the corner of the building. Eventually his hands felt the smooth round cricket wickets. Kasim rushed to the garage door and pushed it with his shoulder. THUMP! Although he applied force the door did not budge. He dropped the stumps, used both hands and shoved again. Not the slightest hint of movement. He attempted to shift the door with a variety of different approaches. But it was stuck solid. He was trapped.

Kasim sat down on the lawnmower and began to worry. He wasn't scared of the dark or even being trapped. He was upset for his mum. She needed his help, it was Eid and she was a little upset.

As his eyes panned around the room and he grew accustomed to the dark he became aware of a rustling in the corner.

"A rat," thought Kasim, lifting his feet from the ground and holding a cricket stump out in front of him like a sword. He took hold of a nearby flowerpot and tossed it towards the sound. It hit the garage wall and landed softly on a sack.

He heard the rustling sound again, followed by the faintest meow. Kasim's eyes and ears sparked together.

"Twinkle," he breathed moving towards the corner. He gently bent down and moved a cardboard box out of his path. "Twinkle," he repeated.

There, slumped peacefully on an old blanket was the precious family pet. She looked up at him, meowed again, and rolled her body to the side. As her ginger fur unfurled Kasim could see that it wasn't just a blanket underneath her. Four little bodies lay twitching, nestling into her underside.

"Twinkle, you've had babies!" squeaked Kasim. Twinkle seemed to appreciate Kasim's excitement and purred gratefully.

Kasim jumped up, took a run at the closed door and positively smashed his way out the garage. He darted like a runaway train into the house. He was just about to shout and declare the news when he stopped and deliberately closed his mouth. He decided at that moment to save the news.

That evening was busy, the whole family helped to clean and prepare the house. All of the new clothes, the boy's shirts and Mum's sari, hung beautifully on the door of the wardrobe. Kasim found it hard to contain his excitement. He didn't know what he was most excited about, Eid or the kittens.

Uncle Aqib arrived. Everyone prayed and talked together. Everything was ready.

The following morning Kasim hopped out of bed like a playful kitten and began his prayers. His mother was up already and there was a warmth in the air combined with sweet smells.

Kasim went into the kitchen. His mum smiled and greeted him, "Eid Mubarak."

He returned the greeting and then took her by the hand. She looked a little puzzled as Kasim led his mother out to the garage.

He had little difficulty opening the door. He guided his mum inside and pulled away the box and revealed her darling cat and the fragile kittens.

"Oh Kasim! Oh Twinkle," she sighed.

"Eid Mubarak," whispered Kasim, squeezing his mother's hand.

Thought/Prayer

God of the World,

We are grateful for our special festivals. May we take a full part in the celebrations by helping those around us to prepare.

At the time of Eid we are reminded to extend the hand of friendship to all.

We give thanks for presents that we receive and happy surprises that sometimes come our way.

We take the opportunity to think about the children and grown ups in different parts of the world who are not as fortunate as us because of poverty, war and conflict. May their lives know the joy of celebration soon.

These are our thoughts and this is our prayer.

An illustration for this story is to be found on page 138.

The Magic Stone

Theme: Self Belief

Introduction:
This story is set in India. It is about an archery competition. It tells of Harvinder, a young man who feels he needs the help of some magic to be the winner.

In a time before now in the centre of India an archery competition was held each year. It attracted the most talented archers from across the region. Each year the champion was declared and the prize of gold was presented.

Harvinder was a boy of great talent with a bow. When he was old enough his mother and father entered him for the tournament. They all had high hopes that he would win.

Harvinder took his favourite bow and made his way to the tournament.

On the first day of the event Harvinder's shooting was magnificent, straight and true. He was soon through to the second round and after super shooting, he made it into the final which was due to be played on the third day.

The other finalist was a young man like himself, his name was Navneet. Harvinder knew Navneet and was aware of his ability as an archer.

The two competitors stood slightly apart and took turns shooting. Their arrows hissed and whined through the air to the targets, each landing dead centre with a muffled thump.

After many rounds all the arrows were fired except one for each finalist.

Harvinder fired first. The arrow twisted in the air and missed the centre of the target by a fraction. Harvinder's head dropped as he walked away. Navneet took his mark and shot. His arrow struck the target dead centre. Navneet was champion.

Harvinder was as gloomy as could be when he returned home. His grandfather touched him gently on the cheek.

"Follow me Harvinder, I have something for you," said his grandfather reassuringly.

He took Harvinder to his room and reached into a small metal chest. He pulled out a beautiful smooth grey stone.

"Harvinder, this is a magic stone," announced his grandfather.

Harvinder's mouth opened like a goldfish.

"When you fire your bow, rest your toe on this stone and you won't miss," continued Grandad.

Harvinder took the stone in his small hands. It was cool like a winter morning and smooth like a jewel.

For the months that followed, every time he practised with his bow his foot lay on the stone. The arrows flew like beams of sunlight. Piercing the target's centre every time.

The year passed and Harvinder entered the archery competition once again. Harvinder dispatched every arrow with superb accuracy standing on the stone. The final was a repeat of the previous year and Harvinder found himself matched against Navneet once again.

The final was held on the third day and Harvinder was up early to give himself time to prepare. He pulled on his most comfortable shirt and put his feet into his softest leather shoes. He picked up his slender bow. He then went to the chest that contained the stone.

It was not there.

He went outside, slightly perturbed and found his father looking up at the clouds assessing the weather conditions.

"Father have you seen my stone?" Harvinder questioned.

"No, my son I have not," replied his father.

Harvinder was becoming agitated and he returned to his room. Even though he searched high and low the magic stone could not be located.

It was time to begin the final. Harvinder had to shoot without the stone.

The two finalists stepped up to the mark and each in turn fired. One after another the arrows hit their target centre spot. It was all up to the last shot.

Navneet moved into position. He looked confident, his grip was strong. The wire of his bow twanged as the arrow was released, the air was sliced but the dart fluttered and struck the target marginally outside the centre.

Harvinder stepped forward. If he hit bull's eye he would win. But he had no stone. No magic.

He breathed deeply, took an arrow, placed it certainly on the string, pulled and fired. It zipped to the target, humming like a stinging insect. It struck dead centre.

A cheer errupted. Harvinder was champion at last.

That evening Harvinder found his grandfather sitting quietly.

"Grandad I won," sniffed Harvinder. "I had no magic stone but I still won."

"Harvinder the stone is not magic," said his grandfather, placing his hand on his grandson's shoulder. "I found the stone in the garden. The magic is inside you. All you needed to do was believe in yourself."

"The magic is in me?" asked Harvinder.

"Yes child, believe it," said his grandfather smiling.

Thought/Prayer

God of the World and All People,

Each one of us has great potential, but not always the confidence and self belief to achieve our best.

May we trust our own ability, be certain of our talents and strive to succeed.

May we always be grateful for the help, support and guidance of people who care for us and teach us.

These are our thoughts and this is our prayer.

Theme: The Journey of the Three Kings

Introduction:
Three men are travelling on the most important journey of their lives.

"Wake up my friend, it's time to move on."

The sun had barely risen above the eastern horizon and the three men began to move slowly and lift themselves from their camp beds. They stretched their tired limbs, yawned and looked at the sky. They had forgotten how long they had been travelling. The days all seemed to blend into one extended episode.

However, maybe today was different, they had a sense of being near the end of their journey, close to the final point, the triumph of their quest. Maybe this day.

They ate a simple breakfast, saddled up the animals, carefully loaded their precious goods and set off. They seemed to be moving faster today, eager to complete their task.

They passed people on the dusty road going in both directions. Many folk stopped and looked at the men. They seemed surprised to see the three regal characters travelling this road. Some people shouted out to them asking their business. Some people bowed and gave formal greetings. The three men treated all of the people they met with equal courtesy, politely greeting everyone and then moving on.

The travellers stopped at the end of the afternoon, made a small fire and began to warm some food. As they cooked and ate they talked of their journey. The times they had been lost, the occasions when they had felt tired. But they all agreed that this was perhaps the most important journey of their lives.

As they completed their meal, they looked up again to the sky which was growing darker. They eagerly searched for the stars, scanning the Western universe for their signal. And yes there it was, the single, bright, bold star that had been their beacon from the beginning of their journey.

Today it was the closest it had ever been. It was directly above the small town that rested on the rising land in front of them. This town was where their journey would end, this day.

The three men wandered slowly through the narrow streets. They said nothing, they felt short of breath with the excitement. Their eyes searched the buildings, trying to work out exactly where the beam of starlight fell.

As they turned into a shabby back street, they caught sight of a pool of light radiating from what looked like a shed. They could smell animals, cows, and donkeys. They dismounted their camels and walked, nearly tiptoeing to the opening of the stable.

They fell to their knees as they saw the child. He was so small, so new, so beautiful.

After the longest journey of their lives. This day brought them to the king that they had longed for.

Thought/Prayer

God of the World,

At Christmas many people make special journeys to visit relatives, take time to catch up with loved ones. Christmas cards are sent to old friends. Families sit together for a special meal.

May Christmas be an opportunity to bring people together all around the world.

These are our thoughts and this is our prayer.

Theme: Having a Second Chance

Introduction:
This story is set in The Netherlands. It tells of how a young farmer's son gets a second chance to prove himself.

Jan rose early. The sun was barely showing across the farm yard. He looked out of his window and saw the windmill silhouetted against the pale sky.

He quickly and quietly skipped down the wooden stairs and out to the small barn.

He knew what to do, where everything was kept. He was thrilled and delighted. Finally his father had agreed to him travelling to the market at Gouda. Jan had been given the job of preparing the horse and the cheese cart.

It was dark in the barn, Jan clattered around knocking into the buckets and tools. Jacob the large horse snuffled and stamped at being disturbed.

"Quiet Jacob," breathed Jan as he gently patted the horse's massive neck and scanned around for his harness.

After a good deal of clanking and creaking Jan opened the large slatted doors and pushed the cheese cart out into the farmyard. Jan was already sweating and it wasn't even seven o'clock.

"I can do this, I can do this," he repeated in a whispered chant. He was determined to show his father that he was capable.

Jan was the youngest of three. His two older sisters were always relied upon to help manage the farm. Up to now Jan had been considered 'the baby of the family' and given easy tasks.

Jan tried to coax Jacob out of the barn. He tempted him with a sweet carrot. Finally the impressive animal consented and plodded out and stood obediently beside the cart. Jan strained and pulled as he harnessed the horse to the cart.

Once attached, Jan stood back. Jacob also shuffled backwards.

Oh no! The brake wasn't on and the cart shunted backwards towards the canal.

"Stop, Jacob stop!" called Jan.

He jumped aboard and tugged at the large brake lever. The cart juddered to a halt just centimetres from the water's edge.

"Jan, Jan what's happening?" It was Mr Van de Neever, Jan's dad. "The cart is too near the canal," he continued frantically. "Can I trust you Jan?" he questioned.

"Yes Father, I'm ready for market," insisted the boy.

The farmer tutted and drove the cart forward and then began the hard work of loading the flat circles of cheese on to the cart. Once finished the scene was wonderful. A large horse leading an impressive wooden wheeled cart containing a neat stack of bright red cheeses. Mr Van de Neever smiled and helped his eager son onto the seat at the front of the cart.

It was a short but slow drive to Gouda. As the cart rumbled along the straight roads the sun rose high in the sky. Occasionally a long legged grey heron would flap up from the ditch and fly over the heads of the market goers.

Jan loved going to Gouda. He was always bubbling with glee and anticipation as he entered the town and gazed up at the tall houses with the ornate roofs.

"Jan you take Jacob and tie him up behind the Town Hall. Tie him well, he's always very edgy on market day," instructed Mr Van de Neever.

When they had arrived in the Market Square they had uncoupled the horse and cart. Jan dutifully led the large horse around to an area set aside for horses. He was wrapping the horse's strap around the fence, when Pieter his friend ran up to him.

"Jan, you're here, great, come with me to the market hall," cried Pieter. Jan gave Jacob a quick stroke on his side and ran off with his friend.

Half an hour later the two friends were returning to the Market Square when they saw a commotion in the centre. Some market stalls were tipped over and a group of noisy men were struggling with a horse.

"Jacob!" cried Jan. It was his horse. Jan pushed through the people. When he managed to burst through the crowd he realised the full extent of what had happened. His father was there, angrily pulling at Jacob's reins. Jacob had a carrot in his mouth and several vegetable stalls were demolished. The stallholders were screeching at Mr Van de Neever who was trying to apologise and control the animal.

Jan knew at once that this was his fault. He had not secured the horse well enough. Jacob was always greedy for the carrots and he'd run loose through the market seeking food.

The journey home that evening was the most gloomy time of Jan's entire life.

His father was smouldering with anger and embarrassment. Finally he spoke.

"Jan you will never, never, come to market again. I cannot trust you."

Jan did not reply. His head slumped.

Later that month Mr Van de Neever had to travel to the big farmers' fair in Amsterdam. He would be away for three days. It was obvious as he said goodbye that he was still annoyed with Jan.

The air was turbulent and the clouds moved wildly across the sky. There was going to be a storm. Jan's mother was clearly concerned. Mr Van de Neever was away and she always worried about the windmill during a storm.

The day got worse. The rain started and the wind swelled and whipped the poplar trees. The sails of the windmill were tied down and locked but they creaked and shuddered. Darkness fell and the storm grew more powerful. Mrs Van de Neever and Jan's sisters were silent in the house as they listened to the howling wind and the clattering of the shutters. A hissing crack of lightning followed by thunder sent the girls cowering into the corner of the room. But Jan rushed to the window. He immediately saw two disasters waiting to explode. The windmill sails were just about to break free. The barn door had been forced open and Jacob was snorting at the storm outside.

It was Jan's time to act. He pulled on his thick coat, un-bolted the door and ran out into the mayhem of the storm.

He went first to Jacob. Although it was wild outside Jan was calm and strong. He decisively took hold of the animal's rein, all the time talking to him, rubbing his trembling cheeks. Jan led the horse to the very back of the barn and secured him with a tight knot.

From inside the barn Jan pulled the large doors closed. He had to fight the wind but with every atom of his strength he pulled the large wooden door across and twisted a rope around the handles.

Next he climbed out of the barn and entered the windmill. The gears were grumbling with the pressure of the wind. The brake was loosening. Jan tugged the lever as hard as he could and then rolled a barrel against it to ensure it would not slip. The machinery then lay still. Jan went out again and reinforced the ties to the sails with a chain. The farm was now safe.

Jan burst back into the house and flopped down on the rug. His hair was blown wild by the wind and rainwater dripped from him. His mother and sisters had watched everything from the window and were shaking with fear and gratitude.

Two days later all was quiet and mellow once again.

Mr Van de Neever returned from Amsterdam. He was met by his wife and daughters, who immediately related the whole story of Jan's bravery in the storm.

Mr Van de Neever found Jan in the barn sweeping the floor and talking quietly to Jacob.

"Jan come here," he said gently. Jan approached his father. The big man wrapped his arms around his son. "One day Jan," he said, "this farm will be yours and you will be a wonderful farmer."

Jan smiled and Jacob the horse snorted hoping for a carrot.

Thought/Prayer

God of the World,

We are grateful for the opportunities we have each day. May we always use our time well.

Sometimes we get a second chance to prove ourselves. Let us grasp these chances with true determination and strength.

These are our thoughts and this is our prayer.

Theme: Determination
Introduction: *This story helps us to imagine what went on in preparing the burial mask of King Tutankhamun, the Egyptian Pharaoh. Senat has to demonstrate real determination to complete his task.*

King Tutankhamun was dead. The sadness that spread across the country was like a fog of grief. This young and beautiful prince was asleep now and would begin his journey to the Land of Pharaohs.

Senat, who worked in the casting house knew that he and his team would be busy for weeks preparing the masks and statues for the king's tomb.

Rasis, the chief designer soon arrived at the casting workshop with a painting of the death mask.

"I want this cast in pure gold," he said. "It must be the finest and most elegant mask ever created for our pharaohs."

Senat had never seen a design prepared with so much love and beauty.

"It must be ready by the next full moon, there must be no delay," finished Rasis as he swept out of the Chamber.

Senat looked at his fellow workers doubtfully. It was going to be very difficult to carve the shape of the mask, create the mould and then cast the final object in pure gold. The detail on the mask was very fine and Senat knew the finish had to be flawless.

However, Senat began working immediately. He sent for a large amount of clay. When it arrived he started shaving off big lumps. His sharp knife sliced the clay like butter until the rough outline of the mask started to appear.

It was the next part of the process that was the most challenging. Senat had to sculpt the clay into the exact fine features of the Pharaoh. Each small movement of his fingers was taken with incredible care.

Gradually the image of the king's face took shape. The large fan of his headdress swept away from his face and the vision was amazing. Senat stood back and took a deep breath of relief.

The next task was to create a mould into which the molten gold would be poured.

Over the following two days the clay mask was set in a wooden frame and covered in plaster. Senat was pleased that the process was going so well. Perhaps it was everyone's dedication to the king which influenced their work.

As the men carefully opened up the mould, they could see that the plaster was smooth and the image of the king was perfect. They had three days left before the mask was to be ready. They were on track, Senat could hardly believe it.

Rasis, the designer, arrived to check on their progress. He was a proud man who was never really forthcoming with praise. But Senat could see that he found it hard to conceal his delight when he saw the exquisite mould.

"We shall pour in the gold tonight Sir," said Senat, "and the mask will be ready a day early." Rasis nodded and left Senat and his team to their work.

It took seven men all their strength to move the mould into position for casting in gold. As the men shuffled to the centre of the room one of the men tripped on a chisel that lay on the floor. He fell sideways and let go of the plaster mould. Even though the other men tried to keep hold the mould fell.

The mould seemed to fall in slow motion. Senat cried out. It landed with a crack and the left hand side shattered. Cracked plaster pieces exploded across the floor.

The team stood still and looked at each other with horror. Two of the men put their hands on their heads and ran out of the chamber, as if their lives were about to be taken.

Senat said nothing. He purposely swept the broken pieces to the side and said, "Right, we've got one night, get me the plaster, we'll just have to make a new mould." The rest of the team looked at him with bewilderment.

"We haven't got time Senat," they cried. Senat ignored their protests and began to rebuild the wooden frame around the clay mask.

Long after some of the men had slumped down onto the workshop floor to sleep Senat continued the process. His head ached, his fingers were sore and his eyes were clouded with tiredness. But he was determined. The mask was going to be finished.

Eventually only Senat continued working, all of the other men dropped with exhaustion.

The next morning when they woke they found Senat slumped against the finished mould.

"Senat you've done it, you've made another mould."

Senat could barely mutter a response. He stood up, washed his face with water and signalled to his team to prepare for the casting again.

The molten gold hissed and bubbled as it was tipped into the mould. Not a drop of this precious metal could be wasted. The heat in the room was extreme and Senat was exhausted when the mould was finally sealed.

The finished mask was concealed under a cloth. The door of the chamber swung open and Rasis and some people from the royal family walked in. Everyone was silent as Senat carefully took hold of the cloth. Slowly he revealed the finished work.

A ripple of awe spread across the chamber as everyone looked at the mask. It was the most wonderful, beautiful and haunting image of the king. His smooth features fashioned in glinting gold had a magical quality. The workmanship was unbelievable.

Rasis looked at Senat and the smallest hint of a smile crossed his face. "This is good work Senat, the Pharaoh's image will last forever."

Thought/Prayer

God of the World,

May we be determined to succeed in all of our tasks and activities. May we have strength and purpose in all that we do and not be swayed off track by temptation or laziness.

We think of the many people who care for us and show determination in their work, which helps us all to have a better quality of life.

These are our thoughts and this is our prayer.

An Illustration for this story can be found on page 139.

Lucky Cat

Theme: Luck

Introduction:
In Japan the Maneki-Neko is a lucky cat. These small ceramic ornaments are considered to bring good fortune. They will often be placed in shops and businesses in order to bring good fortune. Ben's Japanese friend gives him a lucky cat to help him with a run of bad luck.

Ben was right out of luck. He had dashed to the sports notice board at playtime and frantically looked for his name on the list for the basketball team. It wasn't there. He hadn't been picked. Later at the end of the day he'd gone to collect his trainers from the cloakroom and found they'd disappeared. They were new and his mum would be so angry when she found out he'd lost them.

The evening was grey and wet. Ben's cagoule was little use in the downpour of heavy rain. The moment Ben undid the zip to allow the water inside to drip down, a car came speeding by and drove through a large puddle sending up a shower of water which completely soaked him.

Yes, Ben was out of luck.

The following morning was not much brighter. He was on his way to school getting more and more soggy, when he suddenly remembered his spelling test. He was supposed to have learnt twenty difficult words for homework, but because he was feeling glum he'd completely forgotten.

Mrs Grant gave the spelling test first thing so there was no time for Ben to even scan over the words. Three out of twenty was his result.

"Dear me Ben, you usually do better than that!" announced Mrs Grant. "What's happened to you?" she questioned looking at his forlorn gaze.

"My luck's out Mrs Grant."

"Luck Ben, I don't think it's a question of luck," she returned.

Ben didn't reply. He had resigned himself to another day of problems.

At playtime Ben sat on the small wall by the kitchen. He didn't feel in the mood for playing basketball or talking with his mates.

After a short time, along came his friend Fumihiko. Fumihiko or Fumey as he was kown, was from Japan. He had come over to England because his dad secured a new job in London.

"You got bad luck Ben?" questioned Fumey kindly.

"Oh Fumey, everything's going wrong for me. I didn't get in the team, I lost my trainers, and failed with my spelling because I forgot," said Ben desperately.

"Don't be sad, I'll get you good luck," his friend sang happily. He gave Ben a firm, friendly slap on the back and ran off.

Ben half smiled at the lively boy and then returned to his disappointed thoughts.

Ben's dad was clearly a little put out by the low score in the spelling test, although he tried not to show it. Ben slumped on his bed wondering if his luck would change.

As Ben arrived in the playground the next day, Fumey ran eagerly up to him clutching a small cardboard box.

"Here Ben, good luck," he smiled, thrusting the package into Ben's hand. Ben took it uncertainly and moved it between his fingers assessing its weight.

"Thanks," stuttered Ben.

He carefully peeled off the sellotape holding the lid of the box in place and pulled out the object inside. It was a white ceramic cat. Its features were happy, painted in red and gold. It held one paw up as if signalling.

"It's Maneki-Neko," declared Fumey.

Ben looked blank, smiled and held up the sculptured cat gratefully.

"Lucky cat," pronounced Fumey, "my uncle has one in his shop in Tokyo, he says it brings good luck and yes his shop is good. He sells many cameras."

"Lucky cat?" answered Ben half questioning, half affirming with his kind friend. "Thanks Fumey, it's er . . . great," he finished.

As Ben walked into class he felt pleased at how generous Fumihiko was.

"Look Mrs Grant a lucky cat," announced Ben with confidence.

Mrs Grant smiled, took the pretty ornament in her hands and ran her fingers over the pronounced features.

Just before playtime Mr Marely came into the classroom and asked to see Ben. "Ben are you available for the basketball match tomorrow?"

Ben hesitated, "Yes Sir, but I didn't think I was on the team list," Ben questioned.

"Well Peter can't make it so you are my next choice," confirmed the teacher.

"Yes Sir, thanks I'll be ready." Ben strode back to his place and ran his thumb over his lucky cat.

Ben's attention was then taken by Lucy walking towards him with a plastic bag held out in front of her.

"Ben aren't these your trainers?' she asked.

"Thanks, yes, Lucy. Thanks."

"Well don't hang them on my peg again," she scolded.

Ben smiled and apologised. He looked at the Maneki-Neko and found himself saying "Thanks."

At the end of the day he scoured the playground for Fumey. He spied him in the corner with his sister.

Ben walked across and pulled the cat from his jacket.

"Fumey, Fumey, it's true, the lucky cat, it's true!"

Fumihiko laughed out loud, his white teeth visible and his eyes sparkly.

"Lucky Cat, Maneki-Neko, I told you Ben."

When Ben ran into his house his mum cheered.

"Do you know about the cat?" asked Ben, slightly confused by his mother's joy.

"Cat? What cat Ben? Your trainers, Ben, you found them!' she was pointing to Ben's feet.

"Yes Mum, the lucky cat got them for me." Ben held up his gift from Fumihiko. His mother said nothing but grinned at her son.

"Maneki-Neko, it's brought back my luck."

"Good boy Ben, good boy," his mother whispered.

Thought/Prayer

God of the World,

Sometimes it seems like we are having bad luck. Things go wrong for us and we hope for better fortune.

Our attitude and outlook can often influence the way things happen for us.

May we be positive and enthusiastic in our approach to our lives so that we can be successful and have good fortune.

These are our thoughts and this is our prayer.

An illustration for this story is to be found on page 140.

Marek and Ursula

Theme: Love

Introduction:
This story is set during the Second World War. Like so many people the two Polish characters in the story were separated because of the fighting. But their love for each other remained strong.

It was the happiest of days when Marek Gynp took Ursula as his wife. As they walked through the streets of Warsaw, Marek held his head high. His beautiful bride on his arm floated in her sparkling white dress like some magical princess in a fantasy land.

But this was not a fantasy. Reality was just around the corner and Ursula knew that very soon she would have to bid farewell to her new husband.

Marek was going West to join the Polish forces in England. The war was close like a wolf at the edge of the forest waiting for the deadly moment.

On the day of his departure for the war Ursula clenched her teeth and bit back the soreness in her throat but the tears could not be stemmed and they trickled down her beautiful cheeks.

"My darling," whispered Marek, " I will be back again soon, this war will end quickly and we'll begin our new life here in Warsaw."

With that the train rattled and shunted out of the station. Marek waved and mouthed some encouraging words to his love, but the salty mist in her eyes impaired her final vision of him.

As the months went by the fighting was ferocious. The bombing terrifying. The ordeal long and hard for everyone.

Marek was a skilled mechanic and his sergeant was grateful to him for servicing the supply lorries that took the essential ammunition and supplies to the front line.

In Warsaw the picture was grim. The invading German army had swept into the city with almighty power and it was no time until ordinary people were rounded up and despatched to labour camps.

Ursula had been strong when she was jostled roughly on to the railway carriage.

"They're treating us like cattle," complained an older woman. Ursula clasped her hand tightly in hers.

"Don't worry,' she reassured her, "we'll be safe."

Ursula and all of the accompanying girls and women were taken to a northern camp. Here they were set to work digging in a quarry.

The days and months became a long nightmare of hunger, tiredness and fear, but inside, her love for Marek was a warm and untouchable place, which gave her strength.

On 5 May 1945 victory was declared. Marek, his fellow Poles and his new English friends laughed, danced and sang through the streets of London. However, there was a low ache of sadness in Marek's soul.

During the war years he had sent letters and messages to Ursula in Warsaw. No replies had been received and when he met a friend who had recently travelled from Warsaw, Marek was shocked to hear that no one had seen Ursula for years.

At the first opportunity Marek boarded a train East. The journey was tedious and uncomfortable. When he arrived in his home town he summoned up all his energy and began the quest to rediscover his wife.

One empty room led to another. All possible contacts who may have known Ursula could shed no light on her whereabouts. The greatest blow of all came when Lara, a cousin of Ursula's, described how she had been taken at the beginning of the troubles.

"I'm so sorry Marek my dear but we believe that Ursula may be dead," faltered the cousin, clutching the broken man as he wept.

'No,' thought Marek, 'I can't believe it, I don't believe it.'

With immense sadness Marek returned to England knowing he would obtain work in the factories.

Three years later as the Warsaw streets began to clear of the scars of war Ursula found her way back home. She had finally been released. She too had only one mission, to find her husband. Although they were married for only a few weeks before the war, her love for Marek was deeper and greater than all the other emotions she had experienced.

Ursula's cousin could not contain her shock and delight when she walked into the apartment.

"Ursula, Ursula we thought you were . . ." she did not finish the sentence.

"My darling Lara, have you seen my husband?" asked Ursula eagerly. Lara told her cousin about Marek's visit and how he had returned to England. Lara took out a crumpled piece of paper and thrust it into Ursula's hand.

"It's Marek's address in England," she declared.

When the envelope dropped through the door of Marek's flat, he thought he recognised the handwriting. "A Polish stamp," he mused. With care he opened the letter.

"My sweet Marek," it read, "I am here in Warsaw. I am alive. I have been kept alive by the thought of being with you again. I am coming to London."

Marek lifted his head. His eyeballs opened wide like searchlights and he let out a sigh that had lain solidified in his heart for two years. His tears dropped like rain and then he kissed Ursula's letter.

Within a few days Marek was pacing backwards and forwards on the platform at Liverpool Street Station. He held his breath as the train drew in. Hundreds of hopeful heads poked out of the windows. The train stopped and a sea of excited passengers spilled onto the platform. He couldn't see her. Where was she? Marek's head was spinning.

"Marek," interrupted a gentle voice, "Marek, here I am."

She was there. The two clung to each other. The war was over. When they eventually released each other Ursula stood back from her husband and looked him up and down.

"Marek," she said clearly, "you need a haircut!"

Thought/Prayer

God of the World,

War is responsible for loved ones being separated. Love is strong and will overcome the most ferocious of wars.

At times we pause and remember the many people who have suffered in the World Wars.

We hope that peace will sweep across the world and that the power of love will mend the conflicts that lead to war.

May the world know peace.

These are our thoughts and this is our prayer.

Theme: Taking Time
Introduction:
Some people always rush everything that they do. Katie is one of those people. Unfortunately because she rushes she makes mistakes. Katie is prompted to make a change.

Katie was always in a rush. She never took her time with anything.

"Slow down Katie," her mum was always saying, "you're going too fast."

But Katie would never slow down. She constantly wanted to do it first and fastest, never waiting for anyone else.

Katie was smart, she was popular, she was clever and very able. She could write imaginative stories, work out complicated mathematical problems, sing, paint, swim. In fact, she was more than equal to all of the challenges at school.

However, on parents' evening her teachers would often say, "Katie hasn't produced her best work, unfortunately she rushed her activities and let herself down."

Katie didn't care and she did not slow down.

But on one particular day at the beginning of the summer term, Katie was to change. The day began as normal. Katie rushed her breakfast, bolting down her toast and spilling her orange juice down the front of her school shirt.

"Oh Katie, slow do . . ." But before her mother had a chance to finish the sentence Katie was out of the door.

"Bye everyone," she shouted.

"Katie, don't I get a kiss?" called her mum. But she was gone, hundred miles an hour down the road to school. She wanted to be first in the playground, to see what was happening.

Margaret, her good friend ran up to her.

"Hello Katie, did you do that maths homework?"

"Yes, simple!" Katie replied speeding up.

"It took me ages," announced Margaret.

"Ages, I did it in ten minutes, no problem."

Margaret wondered whether Katie had completed her homework properly, she knew her friend and how she rushed everything. Margaret bent down to tie up her shoe lace.

"Hang on Katie, my shoe's undone." But Katie did not hang on, she was off without a backward glance at Margaret who was desperately trying to knot her black shoes.

The playground was quite empty when Katie arrived. She looked around for someone to play with, but none of her friends were there. A few spots of rain fell on her which turned into a sudden downpour and Katie was drenched. Gradually the other children arrived in the playground, some with their mums and dads, some older children running in on their own.

She spotted Margaret coming in clutching her other friend Jackie. The two of them were sheltering under Margaret's umbrella eating some sweets. Katie felt left out. She walked across to the two friends.

"I didn't know you had sweets and an umbrella!" Katie accused Margaret.

"You ran on, you didn't wait for me, you always run on and never wait for me," retorted Margaret.

Katie felt hurt and guilty at the same time.

Maths was the main lesson of the morning. Katie motored through the page of questions that her teacher had set. She tried to be neat, but the speed at which she worked prevented her from presenting her work as well as she could. She didn't care, she was the first to finish. She hustled up to the teacher and thrust the completed work in front of Miss.

"Katie you've added these, they are take aways, you didn't read the sign. And look here, oh Katie you've missed out the decimal point."

Katie had a sinking feeling in her stomach. She hadn't read the questions correctly, and even though she knew all the answers she had blown it. Disappointed, but trying not to show it, Katie moped back to her seat to attend to the corrections. In the meantime, Margaret, Jackie and some of the boys finished the work all absolutely correctly.

"If only I hadn't rushed," dreamed Katie and a single tear dropped on her desk.

It was the same story in the afternoon. Katie was so talented at painting. The teacher wanted a few choice paintings to illustrate some sea stories that the class had written. She asked the class to get started. Katie though, instead of taking time and doing justice to her real artistic attributes, rushed the picture.

It was smudged and really not that good. Needless to say, the teacher could not choose it for the display.

That night Katie went to bed, sad and frustrated. 'Why oh why had she made such a mess of the day?'

As Katie slept, she dreamt. She dreamt that she found a bottle of silver dust and that when she took a fistful of the sparkling powder and threw it in the air, she could wish for anything.

Katie's wish was easy. She wished for the day all over again. In her dream she saw herself start the day afresh. She put everything right. Took her time with her breakfast, found time to talk to Mum whilst she ate without spilling her juice. She liked it when Mum kissed her goodbye. She waited as Margaret tied her shoe and was pleased to wait at the corner for Jackie. The three of them went to the shop together and Margaret kindly bought Katie a bar of chocolate. When the rain started the three friends snuggled together under the umbrella, laughing as the drops pattered and splattered on the ground. She felt the warmth of their friendship.

In her dream, during the maths lesson she took her time, read the signs, put in the decimal points and managed to finish all of the worksheet correctly. Her teacher praised her for her care and accuracy. Katie felt magnificent. And yes the painting was beautiful.

The shrill ring of the alarm clock stirred Katie from the dream.

"Time to get up Katie," shouted her mum. Katie scanned around the room for the bottle of silver dust. No it was a dream. She thought about the dream. She was determined to change.

She took her time with her breakfast. Her mum looked surprised when Katie kissed her goodbye and said, "Have a lovely day Mum."

Katie's new day was very different.

Margaret and Jackie were pleased when Katie walked steadily to school with them. They shared some fruit as they talked together.

"Well done Katie, every question right," said her teacher later when Katie had carefully completed her maths. "You've used your time very well this lesson."

Katie looked up at the clock, "Time," she thought, " I think I'll use it better from now on."

The bell rang for play time. Katie smiled and dashed out of the classroom.

"Katie don't run!" shouted the teacher.

Thought/Prayer

God of the World,

Rushing our activities sometimes causes us to make mistakes or miss out on something important.

It is good to be prompt and keep up a good pace, but using our time well will help us to be accurate and considerate.

We shall have each day only once, may we use our time well and not be quick or too slow in our work and play.

These are our thoughts and this is our prayer.

An illustration for this story is to be found on page 141.

Inderveer the Fisherman

Theme: Kindness

Introduction:
This story is about an Indian fisherman who cares for his grandmother. One particular day he catches an unusual fish.

Inderveer Singh owned a small fishing boat. That was all he owned. He slept in a small house near the town of Chatrapur in India. Each morning he would sail his boat out into the Bay of Bengal and try to catch enough fish to feed himself and have some left over to sell on Chatrapur market.

Although Inderveer was not a very good fisherman he was content. He enjoyed the simple pleasures – the sun over the water, the white egrets flying near the shoreline. He would go to the temple and listen to the complex rhythms of the Tabla that were played. Inderveer gave thanks to God for his simple life.

However, he had one worry. His grandmother was old and increasingly frail. She relied on the generosity of neighbours and the good fortune of the family. She lived in a humble house on the road to Berhampur. Inderveer would visit as often as he could and sometimes take fish for a meal.

One warm and misty morning, Inderveer cast off in his small vessel and sailed out into the bay. His nets were ready and he was eager to make a good catch. He wanted to make as much money as possible to be able to pay for a special celebration of Vaisakhi for his grandmother.

Unfortunately as the day wore on and the sun grew stronger, Inderveer caught very little. The occasional crab was pulled up and scuttled across the deck of his boat when it was released from the net.

Inderveer was preparing to return to shore and decided to pull up his net for the last time. All at once his small craft lurched to the port side. Inderveer grabbed the mast to stop himself being thrown over board. He soon realised his net was full. With quivering excitement and great difficulty Inderveer drew up the net. In the mesh of ropes and loops an enormous fish writhed, its green-blue glistening scales catching the evening sunrays. As Inderveer dropped the sea creature on the deck, he suddenly stood back taking in the full shape of his catch. The large tail fin was only half the body, the other half was that of a young woman. Her shoulders were marked red by the net and her long tousled hair dripped. She had large beautiful eyes that were filled with terrible fear. She flinched as Inderveer moved closer.

A million thoughts went racing through the young man's mind. Who was this woman? What was this creature? And what on earth should he do with her?

After a few head-spinning minutes, Inderveer decided to take the sea woman back to the shore. He would get a fine price for the beautiful and strange creature. Inderveer took a rope and grabbed hold of her tail. The terrified creature flapped her tail and covered her head with her small arms. Inderveer stopped. He had a certain and powerful sense of her fear. The good heart inside him caused him to reconsider. He gently and firmly lifted the creature, shook the ropes free of her body and leant over the side of his boat. The split second before he dropped her into the sea she looked up at him. At that moment she was calm. She looked into Inderveer's eyes and smiled. She plunged into the grey sea and with a flick of her tail she was gone.

Inderveer dropped to the deck of his boat and his eyes glazed over. When he regained his sense of reality he saw a knobbly shell in amongst the netting. He lifted it and admired its shape and smooth surface. He put it to his ear. He could hear the familiar whooshing of air, the sound of the sea. The sound changed and the haunting song of a woman echoed inside the shell. The supernatural notes moved Inderveer. He was able to make out words in the music. "Cast in the sunset," sang the voice.

Inderveer was bemused. He looked towards the shore and was aware of the low broad beams of the setting sun in the water. With renewed vigour Inderveer gathered up his net and let it fly towards the sun's rays.

Within a minute the water throbbed and splashed with the bodies of fish.

Inderveer strained every muscle heaving up the full net.

As he landed his catch he was filled with awe. It was the largest and richest catch he had ever made. Plump, fresh and delicious fish weighed down his small craft. Inderveer put up his sail and slowly travelled back towards the lights of the coastline.

That evening it took Inderveer two hours to pack the hundreds of fish into boxes.

He was up like a spring bird the next morning. His cart loaded in anticipation of the market in Chatrapur.

The market had barely started when Inderveer sold all of his fine fish. His pockets jangled with coins as he walked to see his grandmother, carrying the largest fish that he had saved for a meal.

His grandmother greeted him with a kiss. She let out a small cry of joy as she saw the fish. She breathed out a grateful sigh as Inderveer placed a handsome sum of money on her table.

"Grandmother our Vaisakhi celebrations this spring are going to be wonderful," he sang.

"Inderveer you are my dear grandchild. Your heart is rich with kindness," she whispered.

Inderveer hugged the old lady and then lifted the fish saying.

"Come on Grandmother let's cook it, I'm starving!"

Thought/Prayer

God of Land and Sea,

We are grateful for the kindness we are shown. May we too have kind hearts.

Very often an act of kindness requires us to think of others before ourselves.

May we be strong and kind in all that we say and do.

These are our thoughts and this is our prayer.

An illustration for this story is to be found on page 142.

Messages

"My son," said the king, "if you are to show that you are strong enough to one day be king, you must travel from here and find The Golden Book of Happiness."

The prince gazed at his father feeling lost and uncertain. "But father," he eventually replied, "I don't know where to go, I have no idea where to start?"

The king turned and began to walk out of the room. He stopped, twisted his head towards the prince and said, "A message will come."

The king said no more and strode out.

The prince retired to his bed, but he did not sleep, he was restless, scared and unsure. Finally he dropped off to sleep. He snoozed for a few hours and then he was disturbed by a tap-tapping outside his window.

He wiped the sandy grains from his eyes, shook himself down and went to the window. In a tree in the centre of the palace gardens he could just make out the green body of a bird. It had a bright red head. The bird was rhythmically tapping at the bark of this large oak tree.

"A woodpecker," whispered the prince, "that's unusual in our busy garden." Eagerly the prince pulled on his boots and hurried quickly, but quietly outside.
As he approached the oak tree he crouched down, not wanting to startle the bird. He crept on his hands and knees up to the base of the trunk. It was as if the bird hadn't noticed him for it carried on industriously hammering into the wood. The prince looked up as the bird finally stopped. The pretty woodpecker hopped down the trunk a few paces and looked down at the prince. The eyes of the bird connected with the prince's eyes in a deep and meaningful way. With its long silver grey beak it seemed to signal to the place it had been drilling. The prince looked at the patch of hammered bark above the bird's head and saw that the creature had tapped the wood. The prince caught his breath in his throat, as he read engraved in the wood:

GO WEST

"A message!" gasped the young man. The bird then flicked its tail and flew off in the undulating pattern across the extensive palace gardens, over the wall and out.

"West, I must go West."

The prince dashed back to his room. He grabbed his backpack, a sword, his prayer beads and a picture of his mother and then made his way to the stables. He saddled up his favourite horse and rode out of the palace heading West away from the sunrise.

The prince rode all day. The good road eventually diminished until it became only a track. The flat land soon became hilly until he reached mountains.

Occasionally he met another traveller. But as the darkness began to draw in he soon felt completely alone. Isolated and frightened. He found a sheltered spot at the bottom of a steep mountain, made himself as comfortable as possible and shut his eyes intending to sleep.

"I need a message, another instruction if I am to know which way to go to find The Golden Book," he pondered.

He was stiff and cold when he awoke from his night's sleep. He slowly opened his heavy eyes and could make out the quickly darting shape of a small spindly white and grey bird flitting about in the trees to his left.

It was a wagtail.

This busy bird seemed to be constantly ducking down and taking crumbs from the ground, then dashing along to a large flat stone, its long tail wagging like a lever behind it. The curious young man moved cautiously towards the little bird. On the flat stones he could see that the crumbs gathered by the bird were not crumbs at all but tiny stones, white flecks of rock.

The wagtail had arranged them to read:

GO TO THE SEA

The prince rubbed his disbelieving eyes as he read the second message. The bird confirmed the instruction with one last flick of his beautiful tail and sailed away like a flying spoon.

"But which way is the sea?" wondered the prince.

He scanned around looking to the horizon. No indication of the sea but his gaze suddenly rested on the sparkle of water to the West. A river was burbling through the lower lands beneath the mountain.

"I shall follow the river, for all rivers lead to the sea," declared the prince as if addressing his people.

The journey was long, tiring and sometimes wet. But as the prince covered the miles, the river began to swell. He was drawing closer to the ocean.

Eventually the prince sensed the sea. The air had the slightest taste of salt and the wind carried the sounds of seagulls.

Then there it was, the expansive ocean, blue, green and mysterious. The prince's heart jumped but his limbs were tired and he once again made himself as comfortable as possible for the night at the seashore.

A harsh, clattering screech roused him. A heavy winged bird flapped above his head and repeated its cackling call. It was a grey heron.

The prince leapt up. Was this the third message? But the bird paid no attention to the prince's entreating gaze. It flapped on along the coast.

"What is it, where is The Golden Book?" called the nervous young prince. He began to chase the large heron along the coastline. He stumbled on the sharp rocks and splashed in the incoming tide now and then.

And then the prince stopped and looked around in despair. The bird was nowhere to be found. The young man fell to his knees, the exhaustion of his quest beginning to catch up with him. Tears of frustration started to sting at his eyes. All of a sudden he caught a glimpse of the elegant bird, picking its way up the shore and into a small cave.

The prince re-energized himself and chased it into the cave. It was pitch black in the cave and it took many minutes for the prince's eyes to grow accustomed to the darkness.

Next the low rasping call of the heron repeated. He could not see the bird, but listening instinctively, he knew that this message was for him. He pushed deeper into the cavern.

At last he saw it. Sitting high up on a rock ledge, The Golden Book. It looked ancient, as if it had been placed there some long ago time by a prehistoric wizard.

The young man slowly reached up and grasped the heavy volume. He clutched it to his chest and turned to leave the cave. As the prince launched out into the brightness he felt elated. This was it - The Golden Book of Happiness. In this book he would find the wisdom and knowledge he needed to be king.

He slumped down on the first available rock and flicked frantically through the parchment pages. But they were absolutely empty, not a single word, letter, picture, rune, nothing.

He turned and turned the pages until at last he found a single page with some markings on it. He could barely make it out but it seemed that around the border it was edged with pictures of birds. The woodpecker, the wagtail and the heron. And then in tiny writing in the centre, a single sentence which read:

BE YOURSELF AND TRUST YOUR INSTINCT

"Is that it?" thought the prince, "Is that the complete book?" The prince stood up, confused slightly disappointed but set off on his journey home.

It took him days, toiling back on the return route to the palace. As he rode up to the palace gates he heard music, the sound of many excited voices. The walls were decked with bunting. Flowerpots gleamed with bright colours. The prince stopped at the first person he met and asked, "What is the special occasion?" The person didn't recognise the prince for his clothes were dishevelled from his long journey.

"Why, have you not heard? It's the coronation, the prince is to be crowned king. The old king is stepping down to allow his son to take over."

The prince galloped up to the palace, threw open the doors and met his father at the steps.

"Father," he started.

"My son, your time has come. You read the signs, responded to the messages and know the words of The Golden Book. Today you shall become king."

And so it was. The prince was crowned as king and he was always true to himself, he never pretended to be something that he was not. He trusted his instinct and made good decisions. His kingdom flourished and he ruled with wisdom and kindness for many happy years.

And in the palace gardens woodpeckers tapped in the trees, wagtails scurried around the lawn and herons flapped their heavy wings as they flew over the rivers.

Thought/Prayer

God of Sea and Sky,

May we be open to the signals and messages that surround us.

At times we need to use our instincts wisely and trust our own beliefs. We must be confident and have the courage of our convictions, standing up for what we believe to be right.

These are our thoughts and this is our prayer.

An illustration for this story is to be found on page 143.

Muputu's Treasure

Theme: Healthy Eating

Introduction:
This story is set in Africa. Muputu has to make a difficult journey to find the treasure that her tribe needs for survival.

Deep in the African forest a proud and strong tribe, lived and thrived. The Duma tribe had dwelled in this beautiful forest for many thousands of years. They lived peacefully farming and hunting and surviving in harmony with their surroundings.

Muputu, a young lady in the Duma tribe, hoped that one day she would be the leader in her village. She was smart, fast, fearless and also kind. She would make a good leader. She dreamt of leading her people.

But as the years went on Muputu became worried. The furthest reaches of the forest were being cut down by people from the outside world for timber and farm land. The animals that the Duma hunted for food were diminishing and the plants, which provided food were becoming increasingly sparse. Muputu could see the strength of her people waning. She could see the colour fading in their eyes. When a severe drought struck and food was scarce she knew that starvation would take its toll on her people.

Muputu decided she must act to save the dignity of her fellow tribespeople.

Late one evening she walked to the edge of her village. She could hear the occasional whistle of a bird. The moon was high and dots of light sparkled against the deep blue sky. Muputu crossed her hands over her chest and began singing. Her sweet prayer song filled the air.

Her voice faded and all was still. Soon another sounded.

"What troubles you brave one?"

The words were coming from the darkness around her. Muputu was stunned with fear at first. Then the gentle voice sang again; "What troubles you brave one?"

Cautiously Muputu answered, "The strength and health of my people is fading, I seek a remedy."

The reply came almost as a whisper; "Seek treasure in the forest."

"Treasure, what treasure?" continued Muputu. "I have never heard of treasure in this forest."

"The treasure your people need for health, wisdom, strength and long lives exists. Follow the stars to the west and always ask for help. Do not be afraid and do not be troubled brave one." The words faltered and Muputu sensed that whoever had been speaking had gone.

Muputu looked up to the starlit night. She judged where the West was and cast her eye in that direction. There, gleaming and glittering was a small ball of light, a star she had not noticed before.

Muputu took a deep breath and strode out through the dark forest, her way lit by the yellow moonlight and the sparkle of stars.

Before long she found her path more and more difficult to tread. The darkness seemed to flood in on her as the trees became thicker and closer together. Muputu pulled out her jungle knife and slashed blindly at the undergrowth that hindered her journey. But her efforts were useless and it seemed as though she was completely shut in by trees, blind with the dense blackness of the deep night and in danger from whatever predators may be about.

Finally Muputu sank to the ground, put her arms around her head and began to cry. Tiredness and misery overcame her and she fell into a long sleep.

Muputu was awoken by the tingling sounds of bell birds twittering and dancing in the trees above her head. Spears of sunlight pierced the trees. Muputu could see she was in the thickest part of the forest. She knew she was well and truly lost. Even though she was refreshed by her sleep and glad of the sunlight and the pretty sound of the birds, she still felt helpless and hopeless.

Once again she crossed her hands across her chest and sang.

The bell birds replied. "What troubles you brave one?" they sang.

Muputu was amazed. She said to the birds softly, "I seek treasure, the treasure to save my people and make them strong again."

"Follow the sun as it travels west, cross the swamp and do not be troubled brave one." The birds flicked their tiny wings and scattered into the trees.

Muputu stood up, squinted up at the sun and began to move west. The trees gradually began to thin out. Muputu could just glimpse a stretch of water, which glimmered like shiny paper. Muputu had never been very keen on swimming and she felt anxious as she approached the swampy lake.

As she walked she felt the ground become soft and uncertain. She was walking in mud, mud which became softer and squelchier with every step. Muputu's legs moved slower and slower as she struggled against the swamp.

Suddenly her body was sucked down and she was trapped up to her middle. Muputu called out, "Help, help me."

As she shouted she saw a large green and blue snake sliding towards her, bending its body as it moved. Muputu was afraid, she knew that many of the local snakes could kill with one bite.

The snake hissed, "What troubles you brave one?"

Muputu breathed out, "I seek treasure."

All at once many snakes appeared in the mud. They slithered up to Muputu, wrapped around her arms and body and pulled her up. She was dragged like a sledge across the mud flat. When she reached the edge, the snakes released her and said, "Go west into the trees, do not be troubled brave one."

Muputu had hardly stepped amongst the yellow bark trees when she was lifted from the ground. Monkeys had her by the arms and she was flying through the air. From tree to tree they moved, bough to bough, branch to branch.

From a great height the monkeys dropped Muputu. She fell, with eyes closed, bracing herself for the crash. But her landing was soft, on to lush leaves of a gigantic shrub. Muputu looked up.

"Do not be troubled brave one," howled the monkeys as they swung away like acrobats.

One remaining monkey turned back and flashed over Muputu's head calling, "Here is your treasure."

Muputu's eyes scanned around. She was standing in what appeared to be an orchard. The trees, which Muputu did not recognise, were full of fruit. Large sumptuous pears, apples, plums, bananas. Rich red and yellow fruit that Muputu could not identify. All around the area there were low level bushes, bursting with flowers and berries.

The sweet smell was intoxicating, the colours beautiful.

Muputu reached up and plucked what looked like a plum from a branch above her head. As she bit into the fruit, the juice dribbled down her chin. The taste was supernatural. It was the sweetest, richest flavour. Her mouth felt alive and refreshed.

Greedily Muputu finished her fruity meal. She was hungry after her wild journey.

But any tiredness that she should have felt dropped away. It was as if the fruit was recharging her energy.

"This is it!" thought Muputu, "this is the treasure I seek."

Hurriedly Muputu gathered together as much fruit as she could. She picked red apples, selected the brightest golden bananas, pulled brilliant blue berries from bushes. She filled her straw bag with the treasure. Some fruit trees and shrubs had pods loaded with seeds. She plucked some of these and eagerly pushed them into her bag.

Muputu could not remember how she found her way back to the village, but her homecoming was magnificent. After she calmed her family down and assured them she was safe and unhurt, she showed her people the wondrous fruit. Small children stepped forward and keenly filled their mouths with cherries, grapes and berries. The older tribe members squeezed juice from the lush oranges. Muputu carefully saved all of the pips and seeds.

Everyone smiled with satisfaction as they felt the goodness of the fruit enriching their bodies. After a while those with aches and pains felt nimble and alive. Coughs and colds disappeared. Everyone who had tasted Muputu's treasure felt renewed.

With the help of her friends Muputu planted the seeds that she had saved. Over the next few months the tribe tended the new bushes and saplings that grew quickly. It was only a few months more before the first harvest of fruit was cropped. And not many more years before the trees yielded delicious fruit.

And so it was that Muputu's tribe lived, healthy and happy revitalized by the beautiful fruit. Muputu became tribal leader and ruled her people with kindness and wisdom.

As an old lady she would sit in the middle of the village and tell the youngest children the story of how she had discovered treasure. She always reminded the children to eat their fruit and vegetables so that they too could lead healthy and happy lives.

Thought/Prayer

God of the Orchards and Fields,

Fruit and vegetables provide the goodness that we need to help us live healthy lives. May we make good choices in our diet and select foods, which provide a balanced diet.

We are grateful for the many people who grow and produce the food that we need everyday and those who prepare the meals that we enjoy. We think especially of the children and grown ups who do not have enough food everyday.

May the kindness of others help to stop starvation in the world.

These are our thoughts and this is our prayer.

Ngonda's Walkabout

Theme: Appreciation of Nature

Introduction:
This story is set in Australia. It tells of an Aborigine on 'Walkabout' who meets up with hunters.

Ngonda woke. It was his fourth day of walkabout and once again the morning brought the certain promise of unrelenting Australian sunshine, which would burn the sand and boil the dew puddles. But Ngonda had no fear of the climate. He knew how to find shade. How to plan his movements for the cooler parts of the day and where he would find food and water.

Ngonda existed expertly from the land. He would sort out nutritious insects and reptiles. He waited patiently in the gum trees until birds flew within reach and then his super quick reflexes helped him snatch them for a meal.

Ngonda loved the solitude, he felt in tune with the earth. But as he ventured into a copse of paper bark trees he heard an unfamiliar and distressing noise. The revving of trucks driving at speed alarmed Ngonda. The sound was soon followed by something worse. Crackling gunfire rang out through the trees. The lorekeets flapped out from the branches in a panic and kangaroos bounced in scattered patterns across the sand.

Ngonda crouched in the undergrowth and watched as the hunters drove their vehicle at speed towards a gathering of red kangaroos. Their guns popped and a large male roo collapsed, long legs flailing. Ngonda had learnt about the hunters from his father. They did not kill for food, they hunted for sport and some false sense of pride.

After a period of manic driving and shooting the truck stopped and four men jumped out. They had packs and guns strapped across their backs. Each man marched off in a different direction. Every few moments one of them would stop, crouch down and lift their weapon to shooting position. Ngonda braced himself for the bang of the deadly device. He hated the hunters. Not only did they kill the creatures for fun but they broke the spell of peace that existed in the outback.

As soon as he was able, Ngonda crept away from the hunters. Staying low, he made his way towards the river. He knew if he crossed the water he could travel quickly and get out of the path of these merciless men.

He was relieved that evening to lie beneath a banksia bush and hear only the twittering of the bell birds as he fell asleep beneath the stars.

His sleep was ended abruptly by shouts of men. The hunters were near.

"Paul, Paul," they cried, "where are you Paul?" It was obvious one of the group was lost. After much thrashing around stamping and cursing the three remaining men climbed into their truck and sped off towards the river.

Ngonda waited until the engine was gone and then he silently crawled out. He decided to fish in the river for his meal that day. As he walked towards the water he threaded his fishhook. He was just contemplating baked burrendi fish when he stopped. Slumped like an old bag on the floor was the body of a man. He wasn't dead, Ngonda could see the swell of his chest as he gasped for breath.

Ngonda took out his knife and edged towards the man. The gun was dropped on the ground some way away and a cut was visible on the man's leg.

"Help. Help me," croaked the man clutching his leg.

Ngonda put down his knife and examined the wound. It was bad, deep and still bleeding. Ngonda hopped up and ran to the river. He plucked lengths of bark from a tree, soaked it in the river and ran back. With care and strength he wrapped the bark bandage around the man's leg. With more water he bathed the man's face. Finally Ngonda took a bottle from his pack and poured drops of sweet tasting juice into the man's mouth.

After some hours of tending the man's injuries and feeding him baked fish, Ngonda finally spoke. "Are you strong enough to move?" he asked his patient.

"Yes mate, I feel a whole lot better," the man replied.

Ngonda lifted him to his feet. "Your friends are over there in that woodland, I'll take you to them," he said quietly.

After a few stumbling steps the man gradually got into his slow stride and Ngonda moved with him to the woods.

"I will leave you here," said Ngonda and he lowered the injured man to the ground within calling distance of his friends. Ngonda placed a flask of water beside him.

As the Aborigine turned to continue his walkabout the man held up his hand.

"Mate, stop," he cried, "you saved my life, how can I repay you?"

Ngonda looked at him and smiled. "Stop hunting, leave the creatures of the earth to live their lives."

The hunter looked ashamed nodded his tired head and whispered a reply, "I will mate, thank you."

Ngonda stamped the sand in appreciation, turned his back on the man and disappeared into the trees.

Thought/Prayer

God of the Beautiful World,

We are grateful for the wonder of nature. The birds that soar and swoop, the fish that glide and dart, the animals that inhabit all parts of the globe.

May we remember that nature is precious and that each one of us has a duty to respect and protect it.

These are our thoughts and this is our prayer.

An illustration for this story is to be found on page 144.

Michael Such and the Cricket Bat

Theme: Saying Sorry

Introduction:
When Nicky does something rash he has to be strong enough to go back and say sorry.

On Saturday morning the park was empty. Nicky and Ted jogged across the field throwing the ball high in the air to each other. Nicky was catching one handed as in his left hand he had a plastic bag containing the cricket stumps.

The lads found a suitable spot, not too bumpy and with shortish grass, here they pitched the stumps. The ground was dry and a little difficult to penetrate. After a little panting, pushing and banging with a stone, the cricket wickets were set.

It wasn't long before Jagtar arrived. He was lobbing a real cricket ball above his head and catching it skillfully.

"Where's Michael with the bat?" shouted Jagtar as he came close to the two others. The boys shrugged their shoulders and Nicky kicked the stone. Nicky had lent Michael the bat the day before in school and Michael had faithfully promised to arrive at Broad Road Park on time for the morning match. All the boys were coming and it was going to be great. 'A Test Match'.

As the players assembled there was growing impatience. "Still no sign of Michael? Lazy so and so," scoffed Nicky, "I bet he's still in bed."

The group snarled their disapproval and Nicky marched towards the gate. "I'm going to wake him," Nicky shouted in the air determined to get the game going. "It's my bat," he continued indignantly. Ted followed and they soon sprinted round to Michael's front garden.

Sure enough the house was quiet and still. The closed curtains made the whole building seem asleep. Nicky didn't hesitate. He rang the doorbell twice. Ted felt a little uncomfortable. Nicky Gill was a little unpredictable when he was annoyed and Ted didn't want Michael's angry mum confronting them in her dressing gown.

But there was no reply. The house snoozed on. The forthright Nicky thumped the door with his fist.

"Hey Michael," he bellowed, "I want my bat."

The slumber continued.

Nicky bent down and selected a small pebble. Ted stepped forward not sure whether to grab Nicky's arm or try the bell again. But in that moment of Ted's indecision Nicky had launched the stone at the front bedroom window. He intended it to be a clattering alarm call. However, it was like a bomb. The window shattered and small shards of glass tinkled to the ground at the boys' feet.

"Oh no!" gasped Nicky stepping backwards, dizzy with shock.

The curtain flicked violently to the side and a woman's face appeared at the window. She looked both frightened and angry. Ted and Nicky turned on the spot and ran out of the garden. They did not look back, neither did they return to the park. They dashed into Ted's house, jumped up the stairs to Ted's bedroom and quickly closed the door.

After several minutes of nervous conversation the boys walked guiltily back to the park.

A cricket match was in full flow but there was no sign of Michael.

"I've got to go back," said Nicky nervously. Ted watched Nicky walk towards the gate then followed him.

When they arrived at Michael's house, Mrs Such was in the garden sweeping the glass and the curtains were all open. Nicky had woken everyone for sure. Michael appeared and nudged his mother when he saw the boys arriving.

"Well I wondered if you'd return," declared the enraged lady.

"Mrs Such, I'm really sorry," murmured Nicky. He then went on to explain about his bat. He promised to pay for the window, he had saved his pocket money. Mrs Such listened to the whole story nodding silently. When Nicky had finished she replied, "Well Nicky that was a daft thing to do, dangerous as well, but I'm glad you came back to face the music, that took some courage." She took Nicky by the arm and led him inside. "Come on," she continued, "let's get your bat from Michael."

Nicky, Ted and Michael took the cricket bat and joined their friends in the park. The game was tremendous, Nicky was bowling particularly well.

"Have you been practising?" Jagtar asked him.

"You could say that," replied Michael laughing, "he bowled out my bedroom window."

Later in the day Nicky returned to Michael's house, clutching a purse full of money, which he thrust into Mrs Such's hand.

"Oh thank you Nicky but there's really no need," she said with a small grin. Nicky turned and galloped off down the road.

Thought/Prayer

God of the World,

There are times when we must be prepared to say sorry. Often it is hard to find the strength to apologise.

May we always be ready to say sorry when we have done something we should not have.

These are our thoughts and this is our prayer.

The Magic Flute

Theme: Hope

Introduction:
This story is set in Ireland. Oisin longs for a brighter future. When he sees the rainbow he hopes that what he finds at the end will bring him the happiness he wishes for.

Oisin ran up to his uncle, so excited.

"Uncle Tageen, Uncle Tageen, look, look a rainbow." Oisin was pointing at the misty arch of colour in the sky. Tageen put his hand on his nephew's shoulder and sighed.

"Ah it's a beautiful sight Oisin. A magical thing. They say if you find the end of the rainbow you'll find treasure. Gold." Tageen's eyes had a deep and far away look in them.

Oisin tracked the colourful air down to the ground trying to work out where it landed. Where the gold would be. In an instant the light faded a little and the rainbow shimmered and was gone.

It was a difficult time for Oisin and his family. It seemed like they were always poor and always hungry. The potatoes were rotting in the ground and everyone around had a weary expression on their faces. But Oisin cradled his excitement. The weather was drizzly and often rainbows would be projected onto the sky. He would find that gold. He knew he would.

Sure enough on the next showery sunny morning Oisin trembled as he saw the curving bands of colour sweep across the sky. Once again he followed the route of the rainbow as it fell to earth. It seemed to land in the O'Malley's Wood on the brow of the next hill. Oisin took off at a fast pace. Soon he was in the wood trying to run and glimpse the sky at the same time.

He stopped in the centre. 'This must be the place where the rainbow ends,' he thought. Oisin stood still.

A faint sound hummed between the trees. Oisin moved stealthily towards the music. It was a flute or a whistle being played. The notes were sweet and seemed to be moving on waves through the leaves. Oisin wondered who was playing this beautiful music.

He crept even more slowly towards the sound. As he drew closer he was aware of the coloured mist that seemed to drop through the trees. This was the end of the rainbow he realised. He then caught sight of a small, happy-looking man dressed in a green jacket with large buckles and wearing a neat hat.

This little man held a small tin flute to his lips and was playing the lilting music. All around the man, the colours of the trees, leaves and flowers were bright and dazzling. Oisin began to move towards the man. The little chap caught sight of Oisin and suddenly scurried away in a panic. He tripped as he ran and the flute flew from his hand and landed on the ground.

"Don't be scared," called Oisin. But the man had gone. Oisin bent down and picked up the flute. It was light, warm and very shiny. Oisin pushed it into his pocket and set off home.

No one was in the little house where he lived. It was a gloomy day and the house was dark. Oisin sat in his dark kitchen and lifted the flute from his pocket. He put it to his lips and began to blow. He fingered the notes gently and the sound was smooth and strange. As he played a random tune, the air seemed to fill with light and colour. The dim room soon grew bright. The paintwork seemed new and shiny. The scruffy plants in pots filled up with life and their leaves glistened. Oisin's mother came in from the garden and stood gazing at the gleaming colours of the room.

"Oisin, what has happened?" she questioned looking delighted and confused. Oisin tried to explain about the rainbow, the man and the flute, but his mother wasn't listening. She was walking round her new kitchen smiling at the clean and beautiful surroundings.

After a short while Oisin's mother set about baking. She made a pie and several loaves of soda bread. When she was finished she wrapped up the loaves and said to her son, "Oisin, I want you to walk to Aunt Eileen's and take her this bread. She is very low on food."

Oisin knew that his aunt's potatoes had caught the blight and she was facing a bleak time. He walked for quite a while and it was late afternoon when he arrived at his aunt's farm.

Aunt Eileen was not in her house, so Oisin started to walk across the farmyard to her field. Oisin could just make out a person slumped on the ground in the middle of the field. He walked up and saw that it was his aunt.

She was crying, her shoulders moving with the deep sobbing. In her hands she had the smelly remains of a rotting potato plant. She turned and saw her nephew. "Oh Oisin darling, even these plants are rotten, we have no food left," she cried. Oisin bent down and placed his hand on her shoulder not knowing what to say.

After a few minutes he pulled out the flute. He began playing quietly. His aunt didn't move. As he played, the air seemed to fill with colour again. The ground warmed and the dead leaves of the diseased plants trembled with life. It was like all the months of Spring condensed into an instant. The plants became rich and green again. Flowers bloomed and a sweet scent wafted across the field.

Eileen lifted up her head and gazed at the new plants around her. She scrabbled in the soil and pulled up one of the nearby shoots. As she lifted it, small, perfectly formed potatoes dropped from the roots.

"Oisin, what is happening?" she gasped. Oisin laughed and began frantically pulling up the plants. Soon they had harvested a huge pile of beautiful potatoes.

That evening Eileen, her children and Oisin enjoyed a delicious meal.

Eileen said nothing about the flute and Oisin kept it concealed in his pocket.

The next day Oisin called at his uncle Tageen's house. He sat down and told his uncle the whole story. Tageen listened attentively.

"Oisin you have found something truly magical," said his uncle, "but you must give it back, it must be returned."

Oisin was a little confused but realised that his uncle was right. Oisin then kept the flute with him at all times until the rain fell again and the rainbow appeared in the sky.

Once again he ran to the end of the colourful arch, which seemed to be on the bank of a nearby river. Oisin hoisted the flute above his head and threw it with all his strength towards the colours. Soon he heard music being played. The rainbow faded and the sound stopped. Oisin felt alone. He went to the edge of the river and bent down. On the ground there was a small bag. He picked it up and emptied its contents out. A number of small golden coins dropped into his palm. Oisin smiled with delight and turned and headed home.

Thought/Prayer

God of the Changing Seasons,

We all have hopes and dreams for the future.

Maybe some of our dreams will come true. Perhaps our hopes will all be realised.

May we be enthusiastic about a bright future and work hard to achieve our goals.

May we also be realistic about what is possible and remember to be considerate in all of our dealings with others.

We think especially of the children and grown ups who live with fear and conflict. We hope that their future will be brighter and more peaceful.

These are our thoughts and this is our prayer.

An illustration for this story can be found on page 145.

Theme: Achieving Your True Potential

Introduction:
Jenny discovers that her dad achieved something very special - his personal best.

The picture on the wall showed a man running. His face showed the strain of the race. Jenny knew the picture very well. She saw it every day as she came down the stairs. The picture was of her dad, taken many years earlier when he was younger.

Jenny's dad had never spoken to her about the photograph, but every now and then she saw him looking at it and smiling. She wondered about the photo, why had her dad been running, was it a race, where was it, was her mum there somewhere?

One bright Spring morning she came down the stairs and found that the photograph had gone. Jenny's mum had taken all the photos and pictures off the wall and was cleaning the frames. She picked up the photo of the runner and said, "We don't need this old photograph on the wall any more, let's put up one of your school photographs in its place."

"No!" Jenny replied quickly, "that picture is special to Dad, that was a race that he must have won"

"Won?" her mum replied, "I don't think he won the race."

"Dad?" said Jenny later when her father was sitting down in the living room, "What's this picture about?" She took the photograph from behind her back and held it in front of his face. He smiled and looked both puzzled and embarrassed at the same time.

"Ah well that photo is quite old, do you know who it is?" he asked her, teasing.

"Don't be silly Daddy it's you, when you were younger," she laughed. Jenny's dad suddenly jumped up and went over to the desk. He rummaged frantically through one drawer, sighed, closed the drawer and then rifled through the next drawer.

"Here it is," he called out. As he turned Jenny could see that he held a metal object in his hand. "What's that, what have you got?" enquired Jenny, rushing over to him. He held up a lovely golden medal hanging on a colourful ribbon. He looked proud and his eyes glinted almost as much as the medal.

"This," he said triumphantly, "goes with that photograph."

They both sat down together. Jenny's dad began to explain. "I ran in this half marathon race twelve years ago. This is a photo of me crossing the finishing line."

"I knew it, I knew you'd won, I told Mum that it was special, you won and were awarded the Gold medal, well done Dad, you're a gold medal winner!" Jenny jumped around with the medal in her hand. Then she ceremoniously placed it over her dad's head.

"No Jenny, listen, I didn't win," he said reluctantly, "look at the photo." He pointed to some writing and figures below the photograph. It had his name, Graham Peters, and then a number 1327, next it had a time recorded 1 hour 58 minutes and then it read PB.

"I didn't win Jenny, my position in the race was one thousand, three hundred and twenty seventh, look 1327," he continued pointing at the number.

"But you got the medal," protested Jenny.

"Everybody who finished got a medal," he replied. Jenny put down the medal and photo and looked a little disgusted.

Her dad smiled and put his hand on his daughter's arm. "Jenny I never expected to win, I just wanted to do my best and look," he pointed to the 1 hour 58 minutes PB. "That was the best time I'd ever run, I covered 13 miles in an hour and 58 minutes, I was delighted. I had never run that quickly before," he continued.

"But what does PB mean then?" Jenny asked.

"PB means Personal Best, that was the best race I ever ran, I'd run a few before that one, always slower and I've run a few since, but that was my best. That's why I keep the photo on the wall."

Jenny looked at her dad, she didn't really understand. He saw that she was puzzled.

"Jenny I would have loved to have won that race, but I knew that I wouldn't, the most important thing for me was to run faster than I had ever run before. You don't have to be the best, you must just do your best and I did that day and I'm very proud."

Jenny put her arm round her dad's shoulders. "I'm proud of you too Dad. A personal best of 1 hour 58 minutes, that's fantastic."

Graham smiled the biggest smile. "Thanks Jenny," he said and dabbed away a little tear that had formed in his eye.

"So what's your PB Jenny, what are you proud of?" he asked his daughter. Jenny thought for a moment, looked around the room as if searching for another picture and then called out.

"I know Dad, you remember when I wrote that story about the princess at school and Miss said it was my best story that year?"

Her dad nodded, "Well, that was my PB. I'm really proud of that."

"That's tremendous Jenny, and you know you'll have many more PB's. It takes hard work and perseverance, but I know you'll have many more Personal Best occasions to be proud of."

"I hope so," Jenny answered and carefully placed her dad's photograph back in pride of place on the wall.

Thought/Prayer

God of the World,

We are all capable of achieving great things. However, we will not all be the best at something, win the race or be top of the class. What is important is that we do our best and achieve our potential.

May we persevere with every task that we face and put in the maximum effort so that we can be truly proud of what we do.

Take a moment to think of those children around the world whose opportunities to achieve are hindered by war, poverty and starvation. May their lives and life chances improve.

These are our thoughts and this is our prayer.

Pet Day

Theme: Making Amends

Introduction:
When Pet Day is held at St Joseph's School in Trinidad things don't go as smoothly as Miss Harris had hoped.

Arthur lived in Trinidad. He went to St Joseph's school in San Fernando. There were forty children in his class and school was hard, it was hot and often boring. But today Arthur was so excited. Today was Pet Day at St Joseph's. He had taken such great care of his pet snake and he was thrilled that Miss Harris had invited all of his class to bring in a favourite pet.

But Miss Harris had warned a few of the class not to bring certain animals. Last year Bobby's bulldog caused havoc by eating Mary's parrot. Matthew's duck Bernie was mad, or so Miss Harris had declared when it ate the chalk and pecked Mrs Bell, the headteacher, on the bottom. "No ducks this year Matthew," commanded Miss Harris.

The playground was like a market place that morning; practically every child in class 4H had a box or basket containing an animal. Arthur heard squeals of fear and delight as some of the more rare contributions were taken out and displayed. Arthur saw Matthew rushing into the playground. He had a large basket in his hands, but also his jacket was bulging.

"Matthew have you got Tiger?"

"Yes indeed," shouted his friend, opening the lid of the basket and revealing a one-eyed ginger cat.

"And what's under your coat?" inquired Arthur prodding at Matthew's bulging jacket.

"Say nothing," he whispered, "it's Bernie."

"Oh no!" replied Arthur. Bernie was the biggest and angriest of Matthew's flock of crazy ducks. As if to confirm this, Bernie poked his head out between the buttons of the coat, squawked a quack and snapped at Arthur's fingers.

Matthew desperately pushed the bird's head back in against his chest and followed the line of animal-bearing children into the classroom.

Normally the classroom was arranged with desks in straight rows. The children sat and recited their tables or read from the blackboard. Today Miss Harris had moved the desks to the side and arranged the chairs in an inclusive circle.

"Place your boxes and baskets at the side and sit down everyone," shouted Miss Harris with authority. Miss Harris went on to explain that they would look at the creatures one at a time. "We are having a special treat today. Mrs Bell has promised to bring in some of her tropical fish to show us," continued the teacher.

The morning was brilliant. As each child took out their pets the children learnt all about the great variety of animals. There were no real problems except when Michael's spider monkey skipped out of his cage and climbed up to the lampshades. Miss Harris had to coax him down with some grapes that she was saving for lunch.

"I love Pet Day," declared Arthur at lunchtime.

Unfortunately the success of the occasion did not last. As promised, the headteacher arrived with a large tank, which she placed in the centre of the circle on a table. "Listen carefully class, I'm going to tell you all about these beautiful fish that swim in the sea all around Trinidad," she said. It was as if the word "fish" woke Bernie the duck from his slumber. Before Matthew's jacket could hold him back Bernie burst out and flapped across the classroom towards Mrs Bell. Mrs Bell spied her attacker and jumped back with a scream. But Bernie did not want to bite the headteacher, he had his duck eye on the enchanting colourful fish that glided like animated tissue paper around the tank. With an alarming commotion of splashing water, clinking of glass, cackling of the duck and sighs of the children, Bernie seized the largest blue angel fish in his beak and made for the door. Mrs Bell had recovered from her initial shock and let out a roar. "Bring back my fish!" she cried.

Any visitor to St Joseph's that day would have witnessed the most bizarre scene. From the classroom door came Bernie half waddling, half flying with a writhing blue fish in his beak.

He was followed at speed by Mrs Bell who was a large powerful lady. She was trying to run but her running days were long gone. A terrified looking Matthew exploded out of the door next followed by many other children laughing, crying, pointing and dancing. Michael's spider monkey who escaped again amidst the confusion had climbed out of the window and was swinging on the climbing frame in the playground, as if willing the children to play or chase him. Just when you thought things could get no worse, Bobby's bulldog came racing into the playground and chased the whole crowd snapping and barking. His moment had come.

After two or three laps of the playground Matthew managed to jump on the screeching Bernie and prise the blue fish from his beak. Someone immediately dropped it into a bucket of water and it swam around as if nothing had happened.

Mrs Bell however did not recover so readily. Miss Harris sat her down with a glass of water, apologising and stroking her shoulder nervously.

Mrs Bell then ordered all of the children and Miss Harris back into the classroom except for Matthew who she sent home with his deranged duck.

The class was still and silent when Mrs Bell entered. Only the occasional tweet of a bird could be heard as she stood looking around at the children. "Pet Day is a good idea," she said, "but some people here have disobeyed our instructions and so it will never happen again."

Arthur's heart sank. He hadn't even got to show his snake and now the day had been cancelled. In glum silence the children gathered up their pet containers, said goodbye to Miss Harris and went home.

Arthur met Matthew at his back door. Bernie was happily pecking his way around the yard. He let out a triumphant quack when he saw Arthur.

"What were you thinking Matthew? You were told not to bring the bird," said Arthur in an exasperated tone.

"I know, I'm so sorry Arthur, but I thought Bernie had calmed down," replied Matthew apologetically.

"Now Pet Day has been cancelled," protested Arthur, "it will be back to tables and handwriting everyday."

The two friends sat on the stone in front of the house and watched the warm rays of sun sink lower over Trinidad. They had to think of a way of making up for Matthew's wrongdoing.

After hours of frantic discussion the two boys dashed into the garage at the back of the house. They closed the door and all that could be heard was scraping, cutting and the swish of sandpaper. This activity continued during the weekend.

On Monday morning the two boys waited patiently outside Mrs Bell's office. The formidable headteacher arrived on the scene carrying a leather case and lots of paper.

"And how can I help you gentlemen?" she asked, spying the small boys.

"We've brought you this," offered Matthew nervously. He tentatively held a small package aloft to the woman. Mrs Bell put down her bag and paperwork and lifted the package. She turned it over and then began unwrapping it. From the box she carefully took out a wooden carving. It was an angel-fish expertly fashioned in wood. The sculpture was delightful.

"We wanted to say sorry for the disaster on Pet Day Mrs Bell."

Mrs Bell looked from the wooden fish to the sheepish eyes of the boys. "Well boys I am grateful and I accept your beautiful gift and the apology."

The boys were silent.

"As for Pet Day next year," she hesitated, "we'll see."

Thought/Prayer

God of the World,

Sometimes when we apologise we have to make amends. People appreciate a gesture of genuine sorrow.

Let us think of times when we have needed to apologise and make amends in some way.

We think especially of people who have fallen out and friendships that have not been restored.

May we have the strength and willingness to be sorry and make up for any wrong-doing.

These are our thoughts and this is our prayer.

An illustration for this story is to be found on page 146.

Pat's Cup Final

Theme: Every Cloud has a Silver Lining

Introduction:
Just when you feel that things are going wrong an unexpected delight comes along. Often this happens because of the consideration of others.

"Crystal Palace, Crystal Palace we'll support you ever more, we'll support you ever more."

Pat was standing on the desk in the English room, singing and waving his Crystal Palace scarf above his head. He was so caught up in his celebrations that he didn't notice Mr Mason come into the room and the rest of the class go silent.

"We're going to Wembley," Pat continued his chant, "we're on our way..." his voice faltered and he looked around at his quiet, embarrassed and slightly amused class mates.

"O'Reilly sit down at once," shouted Mr Mason, "and report to me for detention this afternoon."

Pat dropped his scarf and acknowledged his teacher with a gloomy obedient look. However, when Mr Mason turned away Pat beamed a broad smile to his friends. Nothing could squash his delight. His team, Crystal Palace were in the cup final and his cousin in London was getting him a ticket.

Pat listened resolutely to Mr Mason as the teacher lectured him about appropriate behaviour in the classroom. Pat apologised and decided not to try to explain about Crystal Palace's chances in the cup final. Pat eventually left the school and dashed home.

He had to make all the arrangements for the cup final the next day. Pat was sixteen and his parents were allowing him to travel by train to London on his own. He had planned to meet Billy at gate C of Wembley Stadium at one thirty on Saturday. The F.A. Cup Final was only a few hours away.

The railway carriage was hot and sweaty, but the atmosphere was tingling with cup final anticipation. Groups of Crystal Palace fans ran and laughed. They punched the air with excitement. The train guard had to tolerate their jokes and high spirits, but everything was good humoured. The guard ended up checking tickets with a Crystal Palace scarf wrapped around his shoulders and a woolly cap on his head. Pat loved F.A. Cup fever, it was infectious.

When the train arrived at Euston Station, Pat knew he had to get the underground train across London to Wembley. Pat had never seen so many people.

Everywhere he looked, the escalators, passageways and roads were jammed with crowds of people. Amongst them Pat saw the familiar colours of his team. Pat boarded the underground train for Wembley and felt that he knew what it was like to be in a tin of sardines.

The tube train was painfully slow. It stopped and waited at every single station on the long journey. Some passengers were becoming impatient and were complaining and sighing. Pat was getting worried. It was one o'clock and he was due to meet Billy in half an hour. At the next station the train waited again and the minutes were rolling by.

With a rush of determination Pat forced his way through the pack of people and off the train. "I'll walk," thought Pat impatiently, "it's got to be quicker than this."

He ran up the moving stairs and out into the sunlight. He was relieved to be out in the air. He scanned round looking for the signs to Wembley Stadium. He fully expected to see a wave of football fans sweeping along the main road to the match. But this was Saturday afternoon and the majority of men, women and children around him were going about their usual busy Saturday business. Pat had mistakenly thought that everyone on the planet was obsessed with the match.

It was twenty-five past and Pat started to panic. "Excuse me," he asked a lady urgently, "Could you direct me to Wembley Stadium?"

"You'd be best to get the tube train," declared the woman, "the station is just over there." Pat followed her pointing finger and looked back at the station, which he'd just come out of.

"Thanks," he hissed.

Beads of sweat broke out on his forehead as he galloped back down the stairs to the underground platform. Eventually a train rumbled into the station. Pat boarded. It was two o'clock. Surely Billy would wait. But oh what a long and tedious journey! Pat's F.A. Cup fever was now turning to a feeling of real sickness in his stomach.

When he finally arrived he joined a handful of late fans that jogged up the main road towards the stadium. He found gate C and nervously searched for his cousin. By now it was only fifteen minutes to kick off.

"Billy where are you?" Pat thought out loud. "Billy please be here!" he prayed.

Five minutes to go and the exterior of the magnificent stadium became strangely quiet. A handful of police officers and stewards skirted around the gates.

Pat felt very alone and completely deflated. He had travelled hundreds of miles, his team had reached the cup final and he was in the street with no ticket.

He dropped to the ground and squatted on the kerb. His head fell into his hands and he heard the low throbbing of the crowd inside as they anticipated the imminent kick off.

"I'm sorry son," said a clear voice, "you can't sit here." A policeman was looming over Pat. Pat raised his head and looked up totally depressed. Pat didn't say a word even though he felt disgusted. He got up and began to plod off.

"Is something wrong?" asked the police officer. Pat turned and croaked out his story, explaining how Billy was inside the ground with his ticket.

The police officer listened attentively and then told Pat to stay where he was. He walked off briskly and entered an office at the side of the stadium. He soon returned to Pat and thrust a ticket into his hand. Pat looked at the ticket and then gazed up blankly at his uniformed friend.

"The thing is, we have a few tickets returned to us that have not been claimed. You may as well have this one."

Pat fumbled for some money in his pocket, but the officer put up his hand. "No thanks son, I couldn't and I wouldn't," he smiled. "Now go on, the match has just started."

Pat felt a wave of wonderful joy and relief. He shook the policeman's hand and dashed to gate C. He stumbled onto the stand and feasted his eyes on the pitch.

The final was closely fought and even though Crystal Palace lost, Pat considered this one of the happiest days of his life.

Thought/Prayer

God of the World,

Just when things are going wrong we suddenly find something to cheer us up. We are grateful for the happy times that we enjoy.

We take time to think especially of those people who live with sadness and disappointment. May their clouds have silver linings and may they have some joy and celebration.

These are our thoughts and this is our prayer.

An illustration for this story is to be found on page 147.

Theme: Remembrance of the Great War / Diwali

Introduction:
This story is set in The First World War. It tells of two diggers who are good friends. Amrit is from India and he prepares to celebrate Diwali in the trenches.

Joey Tanner had been in the Trenches for 3 months now. Everyone had said that the war would be over by Christmas. However, Christmas had come and gone and things seemed to be getting worse.

Joey was a digger. His job was to dig out trenches, dig tunnels and also sometimes dig graves for those young men killed in the fighting. Before the war Joey had lived with his dad in North London. He had been proud when he'd said goodbye to his dad when he was going off to fight. He remembered the tear that trickled down his father's cheek. He had never seen his dad cry. He missed his dad now. Joey was cold, hungry and often frightened. The conditions in the trenches were very poor indeed. The mud and water was up to their knees, rats ran along the makeshift tents and all of the meagre food tasted of mud.

Joey knew many of the young soldiers who were fighting for their country. Some were loud, some quiet, others were scared. Everyone was uncertain what they were fighting for.

Joey became upset when someone he knew was killed by a shell or a bullet.

Amrit Rajput was Joey's best friend. Amrit was a digger like Joey and they were always together, helping one another, cheering each other up when the rain fell and the bullets fell like rain.

Amrit lived in London also. His family were from India. He spent hours talking to Joey in the darkness, telling him about the beauty of India. About the busy towns, the wide River Ganges, special celebrations, the colours and the food.

"One day Joey," said Amrit, "I will take you to Delhi, where my family are from. I will show you wonderful things. We will share delicious food together. We will feel the bright sunshine on our backs. We will forget about these trenches, this war and all this mud. We will be happy. My country is a peaceful place."

"I'll look forward to that Amrit," replied Joey with a smile.

"Look Joey," said Amrit holding up a small candle, "this is a Diva, I will light it next week to celebrate Diwali. I will tell you the story of Rama and Sita and I can think about my family at home celebrating."

"I'd like that Amrit," said Joey taking the small Diva light in his hands, "I'd like to celebrate Diwali with you."

That night the sound of gunfire pounded the skies above the trenches.

Early next morning the sergeant called Joey and Amrit.

"Corporal Tanner, Corporal Rajput, we need a tunnel constructed out of the main trench heading West. We need to plant some mines as we expect the enemy to attack tomorrow from the West. Take your team and get digging."

"Yes Sergeant," replied the soldiers and quickly gathered their tools together.

They began almost immediately digging into the soft earth. Soon a long tunnel was taking shape. As they dug out the tunnel they used wooden slats and pillars to hold it up. Every now and then they would stop to rest or light a new lamp. Trickles of mud would occasionally fall from the roof of the tunnel.

"Is it safe Joey?" asked Amrit.

"Yes my friend, come on, we must get this finished by tomorrow, the sergeant says the troops are moving out tomorrow, come on, keep digging," replied Joey enthusiastically. He seemed to have the strength of ten men as he thrust his spade forward into the mud. Joey was digging so quickly that he soon was well ahead of Amrit and the rest of the team.

Suddenly everyone stopped. "What's that?" whispered Amrit. A rumbling was heard and felt all the way along the tunnel, "Joey I think the tunnel is not safe," hissed Amrit.

"Don't worry, come on, keep digging," replied Joey and he drove his spade into the wall of soil. The low throbbing sound of earth moving rumbled above them and then all of a sudden tons of earth fell into the tunnel.

"Everyone get out," screamed Amrit. The team of diggers scrambled backwards throwing down their spades. As they rushed along more soil fell, blocking the tunnel behind them.

Within minutes the men reached the surface and pushed themselves out into the air, coughing and spluttering.

"Where's Joey?" asked Amrit frantically looking around for his friend.

He was nowhere to be seen.

The sergeant ran forward looking both worried and angry.

"Corporal Rajput, what happened?"

"The tunnel collapsed and Joey Tanner is still in there, we must go back in and dig him out Sergeant," shouted Amrit.

"I'm afraid not Corporal, he'll be lost with all that soil. We must leave the trench. The enemy are moving quickly towards us," answered the sergeant.

"But Sergeant," called Amrit with panic in his voice.

"I said no Corporal," retorted the sergeant. "Now men gather up your tools and let's get out."

Deep in the tunnel Joey Tanner woke up. He felt the soil all around him and as he spat out the mud that blocked his mouth he realised that the tunnel had collapsed. Slowly he began to move his hands and arms scraping at the soil trying to make some space. As he reached out he felt the handle of his spade. Although space was limited he managed to dig a chamber in the tunnel. But it was pitch black. He could see nothing.

Back up in the trench everyone had left except Amrit. He was determined to help his friend and he had started digging at the fallen mud. As he plunged through the earth he had a feeling that his friend was still alive.

"Joey, Joey are you there?" called Amrit gently.

No reply. Amrit moved deeper into the darkness. He realised that he had no lamp. But then he remembered and reached into his pocket pulling out his Diva light. He lit the tiny lamp and moved forward. At the same time Joey continued digging himself out. He felt so alone in the darkness. He was tired and worn out and was beginning to lose hope. Suddenly he heard a voice. "Joey, Joey."

It was Amrit calling, but where was he?

"Amrit, where are you mate?" Joey called back, "I can't see anything."

At that moment Joey saw the tiny flickering light of Amrit's Diva lamp.

"I see you, I see you," he called.

"Follow the light Joey, you're safe now."

His feet were heavy, his arms were tired but his heart was full of hope as he moved clumsily towards Amrit's light.

The two friends came together and Amrit reached out his hand for his friend.

"Amrit you came back for me, I saw your light, you came for me," breathed Joey.

"Come, we'll use the light to help us find our way," continued Amrit.

The two soldiers staggered out of the tunnel and into the trench. All the other troops had moved out. Quickly the men left the trench and joined the rest of the soldiers.

The Great War continued and even though Joey and Amrit saw many of their young friends die in the fighting, they survived, digging and fighting.

Joey never forgot how his friend had saved him with his little light.

Many years later Joey travelled to India with Amrit and in November celebrated Diwali. The two friends lit their Diva lamps and gave thanks for their friendship and their safety.

They also remembered the many young soldiers who had lost their lives. They prayed together and hoped that the world would one day be at peace.

Thought/Prayer

God of Peace and Light,

We remember the soldiers who have fought in the wars. Many millions of people have suffered because of war and families across the world have been affected by the sadness of conflict.

At the time of Diwali, the triumph of lightness over darkness is celebrated.

May we spread peace and light by the way we live our lives and may the celebrations for Diwali be happy.

These are our thoughts and this is our prayer.

Theme: The First Christmas

Introduction:
A young shepherd experiences the most memorable night of his life, when he and the other shepherds are visited by the shining figures of angels.

On a hillside near Bethlehem, Philip, the shepherd boy shivered. It was a cold and clear night. But it didn't matter what sort of night it was the shepherds were always there watching over the sheep.

All was quiet with the flock so the Shepherds snuggled under their blankets. Philip pulled his warm fleecy blanket around him and sat in close to his dad.

Philip's eyes became heavy and were just about to close when Samuel came running up the hillside. He stumbled and meandered because he was gazing up at the night sky.

"Look at the star, look at the star," he called.

Some shepherds looked up at the sweeping sky, others huddled closer into their blankets and tried to ignore Samuel's shouts. Philip lifted his head out of his bedding and strained his eyes at the dark sky.

Samuel continued, explaining to those who were prepared to listen, "I've watched this star every night. It has been travelling towards Bethlehem and now it has arrived. It has stopped right above the town."

Samuel was exhilarated with enthusiasm about the stellar event.

Philip was interested and he tried to find the star with his eyes. There it was and sure enough it was tremendous. A bright ball of silver light burning and glittering against the dark milky blue background.

"This is special," he whispered.

Philip blinked. The sparkle of the star seemed to be locked in his eyes. Everywhere he looked still had the trembling light of the star. Philip blinked again. He realised that the twinkling was not just from the star. The whole hillside seemed to be quivering with a silver light, which was growing ever stronger.

As the light expanded a cascade of high notes filled the air. Philip felt a little uncertain. He looked up at his dad whose face was showing a hint of fear.

"Dad, Dad, what is it?" questioned the boy.

"Don't worry Philip, you just lay still," replied his father.

All at once the shining air and the swell of music grew to a powerful crescendo. The shepherds could not look up. They covered their eyes and dropped to the ground.

"Do not be afraid shepherds," sang a beautiful voice amongst the music. "Tonight in Bethlehem a Saviour has been born. Go and visit the new king." The voice was so strong and yet it was lovely to hear.

The light softened and the shepherds were able to lift their eyes again. Standing in front of them was a group of women and men who seemed to be pulsing with light. They had long hair and flowing luminous white robes. They repeated their message.

"Tonight a Saviour has been born. Go down to the town and meet the king."

With that the light swelled again and the visitors seemed to lift themselves from the hillside and float away towards Bethlehem.

"It's true, I knew it," screeched Samuel. "The star is a sign, come on everyone, let's go down to town."

Samuel lifted his cloak and a basket and made to leave the camp.

"Shall we go Dad?" Philip asked his father.

"I think . . . I think we probably should," he faltered.

One by one the bemused shepherds raised themselves and began the descent towards the town.

A beam of light from the star shone down and bathed a building behind an inn.

Samuel was well on the way to reaching the centre of the beam. By the time Philip reached the light he realised that there was quite a crowd of people. They were all gathered in the doorway of a stable.

Because he was small, Philip was able to squeeze to the front of the group and look into the stable.

He wasn't sure what he would see, but he was quite unprepared for the scene that met his eyes.

A simple man and woman sat beside a manger looking at a new born baby who slept silently, wrapped in a cloth. Every now and then the baby made a little gurgling noise and pulled a funny face.

Samuel moved forward. His wife had joined him and she was carrying a new born lamb. Samuel took the little animal and placed it beside the crib.

"For the new King," he murmured. Other shepherds stepped forward and produced presents, loaves of bread, fruit, cake, a pretty bowl.

Philip wondered what he could give to the baby. He had nothing to offer.

His attention was taken by the stamp of hooves and snorting of animals from behind him. Philip turned and there, dismounting from large animals were three very regal men. They were dressed in the most distinguished and rich clothes.

The shepherds parted without a word to allow the important visitors through to the subject of their worship.

Servants followed behind the kings carrying presents. The gifts were breathtaking. A golden box, an ornate jar and a beautiful bowl. The men placed their presents down by the infant in turn. It was amazing to see the large men bowing low before the baby with true humility.

Philip watched the faces of the mother and father. They were so tranquil and happy. But what present could Philip offer the child?

He then pulled the blanket from his shoulders that was keeping him warm. He politely moved into the stable and offered the blanket to the baby's mother. She looked down at the young shepherd and smiled.

"Oh thank you for your kindness," she said, her gentle face shining.

She took the blanket and carefully placed it across the crib. Philip placed his hands on the edge of the manger and brought his face very close to the infant. The child's eyes were open and Philip loved their sparkle. Philip placed his finger into the baby's hand and felt the lovely firm grip of the tiny child.

"This is a special baby," Philip said as he looked back at all of the guests in the stable.

Philip and the shepherds said farewell to the baby and his parents and left the stable to return to the hillside.

Bethlehem was still bathed in starlight. Philip knew that he would remember this night always.

Thought/Prayer

God of Starlight,

At Christmas time may we remember that respect, love and consideration are the best presents that we can give to one another.

Let us be aware that every baby born to the world is precious and must be cared for, no matter who they are or where they live.

These are our thoughts and this is our prayer.

An illustration for this story to be found on page 148.

> **Theme:** Promise
>
> **Introduction:**
> *In 1979 a civil war began in Nicaragua, a country in South America. This story tells of a young girl living there, who is excited about dancing with her cousin in the carnival, but she makes a promise that she finds difficult to keep.*

"Please Mama, let me," Maria begged.

"Oh I don't know darling, you're not really old enough," replied her mother with uncertainty.

Maria desperately wanted to go to her cousin's to practise the dance for the carnival. Last year she had watched her cousin Consuela, dancing in a beautiful costume to the beat of the samba and Maria had sworn that this year she would be there in the lights, swirling to the music – all eyes on her.

"But Mama, Consuela said she would teach me and Aunt Sophie will make the dress." Maria's eyes were filling with tears, her hands were clasped together. "Please, please, please Mama!"

Mrs Casali looked at her daughter's beautiful face, she could just imagine her at the carnival parade. How proud she would be, but what about the soldiers in the town and the rebels who were said to steal children from the street? Nicaragua was not a safe country any more. Would Maria be safe travelling all that way to her cousin's? So many doubts, so many fears for a mother to bear.

"Oh very well my sweet, but you must be back here by seven. You know the curfew begins at eight o'clock and if you are out after that you will be arrested or worse . . . " Her voice trailed off and she looked out into the street, her eyes glazed over for a second.

"Oh thank you Mama, thank you. I promise, Santa Maria, I promise I will be home on time." Maria danced and twirled out of the room and went to gather together her things.

It was true Nicaragua was not the place it had once been now that there was civil war.

As Maria made her way through the streets she went past many broken houses. She encountered the homeless people, some of whom had been badly injured during the fighting and now sat forlorn in doorways.

The atmosphere was tense.

Maria kept her eyes fixed straight ahead as she nervously walked past groups of young, scruffy soldiers. Their guns were scratched and had obviously been used recently. Maria never liked walking through the streets alone, but she was eager to get to Consuela and learn the dance. She was prepared to tolerate the steely glares of the soldiers.

The minute she walked into Auntie Sophie's house she sensed the carnival atmosphere. The Latin rhythms were thumping out of the radio and each room was alive, full of colourful materials, feathers and mirrors.

"Maria, Maria you've arrived!" said Consuela. "Oh Maria this will be the best Carnival since the revolution, we will have the best samba dance in the city. Come with me Maria."

Consuela grabbed Maria by the hand and took her out to a large shady courtyard at the back of the house. Although it was hot the cousins danced for hours. Consuela laughed and giggled as Maria tripped. But Maria was a natural and soon they were co-ordinated and following each beat with magical skill.

"Maria, Maria, come and see," Aunt Sophie had come out to the courtyard and was calling. Aunt Sophie was holding up the most gorgeous carnival dress. It was the most beautiful gown Maria had ever seen. "Oh Auntie it's a carnival, it's a festival, it's, it's..." Maria's words trailed off with joy and excitement. The ladies hurriedly helped Maria try the dress on. She skipped up and down swirling to the music imagining the heat and the pulse of the carnival.

With all of this excitement Maria had forgotten the time. All at once she turned to the window and saw the night closing in. She darted into the living room and gazed at the clock. It was twenty minutes to seven.

"Oh Consuela, I promised my mama, I promised..." she sobbed as she ran out of the house, not even bothering to take off the carnival dress.

The streets were now devoid of sunshine. All of the scrappy shops had their shutters across and the only figures out and about were soldiers.

Maria could not look up. Her small feet tapped on the dusty road as she jogged. Wherever she became aware of soldiers ahead of her she turned into another street. She turned and turned, until she was completely lost.

The darkness was falling and she felt alone and very frightened. She looked up and down the street. Which way, which way to go? She had no idea. Tears filled her eyes and fear ached in her throat. She began to whisper her prayers, calling on Mother Mary to help her.

Eventually she fell to the floor, her prayers faltered and she felt that she would perish. "Oh Mama, I'm sorry," she whispered, "I promised and I've let you down, I'm so sorry. Mama, Mama," she called pleadingly. And her head slumped between her knees.

"Maria," whispered a soft voice, "Maria is that you?" Maria looked up and there standing above her was her neighbour, Chikita. "Maria, why are you wearing that dress, and why are you here? You should be at home," Chikita's voice was urgent. "Come Maria let me take you home."

Chikita's large hand reached out and took Maria's. Her hand was soft. Maria held it tight and felt relief tingle through her whole body. Chikita knew the way and within a few minutes they were approaching Maria's house.

Maria's mother was standing in the doorway, a crumpled handkerchief in her hand, smeared red eyes gazing into the darkness. When she saw Maria and Chikita she dived out into the night.

"Oh Maria," she sobbed and lifted her child off the ground.

"Mama, I'm sorry, I broke my promise." Maria's mother said nothing and carried her daughter safely inside.

Thought/Prayer

God of the World,

A promise is a precious thing. If we make a promise to somebody we should keep it.

May we never be rash with our promises and be sure that anything we say we are going to do we stick to.

We think especially of the children and grown-ups who have had to live and suffer because of broken promises.

May these people have secure lives where they can expect justice and support.

These are our thoughts and this is our prayer.

An illustration for this story is to be found on page 149.

Taha the Refugee

Theme: Being a Refugee

Introduction:
After a difficult time Taha, an Afghanistan Refugee enters Burnbank Primary School, but feels a little isolated at first.

Taha moved slowly into the playground at Burnbank Primary School. There were so many children rushing around, weaving in and out of one another. Parents pushing buggies, mums, dads, grandparents all milling around. All talking and waving their hands.

They all knew each other and Taha was a complete stranger. He backed towards the wall, hoping that no one would see him or challenge him. The door beside him swung open and a lady that he recognised strode out carrying a red notebook.

Immediately she smiled, nodded and greeted a variety of adults and children.

"Hello Mrs Wilson," shouted a small child.

"Good morning Imran," she replied happily. She then turned and spotted Taha.

"Oh Taha there you are, it's good to see you. Is your mum or big sister here?" she asked.

Taha said nothing and edged closer to the wall but at least felt a little more secure that someone knew his name.

Taha was a refugee. He had arrived in England with his mother and big sister Rafia. They had had to leave Afghanistan because of the troubles and Taha's uncle had organised their journey to England.

Everyone had been very kind but when Taha's mother had said that he had to go to school he felt terrified. Mrs Wilson, the headteacher crouched down beside Taha.

"Right," she pronounced, "let me take you in to meet your class teacher." With that she took his small hand and led him gently inside the modern building. The pictures on the wall amazed Taha. So much colour. So many smiling faces. He entered a neat room with blue topped tables and encountered a man wearing a shirt and tie.

"Ah this must be Taha," declared the young teacher. "Come on Taha I'll show you where to sit."

Taha was led to a desk, allocated a peg and shown flat exercise books bearing his name.

'This seems good,' thought Taha, 'but what was the catch?'

Soon a stream of children his own age tumbled into the classroom. They confidently placed their bags and plastic lunch boxes in various places around the room and then all stood by a chair.

A girl who was a little shorter than Taha sidled up to him. She looked at him but said nothing. "Good morning children,' called out the teacher.

"Good morning Mr Kelly. Good morning everyone," the class sang.

"Please sit down everyone while I call the register," announced the teacher. "We have a new member of our class this morning. This is Taha everyone," he continued. "Taha has travelled from Afghanistan and has come to Burnbank School. I'm sure you'll all make him welcome and tell him about everything we do in class 4."

The children nodded. Some smiled. Some children didn't look at Taha but spoke quietly together.

The morning continued. Taha wasn't able to read much of the book the children were sharing but he understood everything that was being said.

At playtime several children came over to Taha. They asked him questions about his journey, his family, did he play football? After he had briefly answered, the children moved away. Taha circled the playground half-smiling at children. He felt isolated and wished it was time to go back to his mother. But he wasn't scared or worried. He knew what it was like to be really scared. When his family had had to leave their home in the middle of the night and walk along dark roads, crouching in bushes when soldiers drove past. Taha had known real fear. Everything was fine now.

A group of boys rushed past him following a ball that bounced at great pace. One of the boys veered off the path of the others and threw himself squarely into Taha. Taha was shocked. He felt the thump of the boy's shoulder and in an instant Taha was flat on his back on the solid playground. "Oh sorry," laughed the boy and ran on. Taha didn't know what to think. His back ached and he felt a little embarrassed.

The bell rang and the children dutifully lined up and snaked into the classroom. Taha looked across at the boy who had knocked him over. The boy was smiling and pointing at Taha in a threatening manner. Taha looked away. The quiet girl beside him looked down at the desk when Taha tried to catch her eye.

At the end of the day the children jostled in the cloakroom. Taha made towards the door when the same aggressive boy stepped in front of him.

The boy took a folded piece of paper and pushed it firmly down the front of Taha's jumper. Taha felt scared again. He ran out to his mother, breathing deeply to avoid tears. It wasn't until later when he was on his own that he retrieved the paper from his jumper. He unfolded it slowly and saw two words printed:

GO HOME

Taha fully understood. He wanted to tell his mother but he knew that they were lucky to have a home and a school and he didn't want to cause more heartache for his family.

The next day, school started with the same feeling of loneliness. At one point during the morning the boy came across to Taha's desk.

"Get my letter?" he spat. Taha did not reply.

"Sit down please David," instructed Mr Kelly. The boy sniffed in Taha's ear and returned to his place. The girl beside Taha looked up at him with a blank expression. Taha knew that she hated him too. She probably wished he wasn't sitting beside her.

After another lonesome lunchtime, Taha returned to his classroom. The lesson did not start as Mr Kelly was sitting talking purposefully to David and some other boys. The boys hung their heads and looked awkward.

Taha's attention was drawn suddenly to another folded letter being slowly pushed across the desk to him by his silent partner. She looked at him with still eyes.

Taha grabbed the letter, he was angry. He had enough. He tugged it open fully intending to scream at the girl when he saw that the letter had attractive patterns on it. Balloons, cakes, streamers. The words read:

COME TO MY PARTY

Taha felt a pulse of shame and delight surge through him.

"It's this Saturday," the child said quietly, "lots of the class are coming, can you come Taha?"

Taha loved the sound of his name spoken so gently. He could barely reply but managed to whisper a response.

"Yes, thank you."

Taha felt welcome.

Thought/Prayer

God of the World,

There are millions of refugees around the world who have had to leave their homes because of war, poverty and starvation.

May these travelling people receive a warm welcome wherever they arrive.

May we sympathise with these people and provide care for any new people who join our community.

These are our thoughts and this is our prayer.

The Christmas Song

Theme: Third World Charity

Introduction:
This story provides an account of how it may have been for one of the pop stars, who was involved in making the Band Aid record in December 1984.

George opened the door to his luxury flat, walked in and slumped down on the large sofa. It had been a busy day and he was tired. He had been in the recording studio since eight o'clock that morning, singing the same song over and over to get it just right for his latest CD.

His flat was fantastic, the most expensive furniture, woven rugs, valuable paintings on the walls. He was a successful singer who had sold millions of records and CD's. He could afford a wonderful lifestyle.

George flicked a switch on his handset and a large T.V. screen sparked on. As George changed the channels he yawned, there was nothing much on that he wanted to watch. He turned over to the news.

Suddenly on the screen pictures of children in Africa appeared. The children were crying. Their arms were thin. They walked uncertainly, stumbling at times. Other pictures showed people lying on the ground. There was a wailing sound, people were obviously in pain. Some were even dead.

"Famine has swept across this country and many thousands are dying," announced the reporter.

George could hardly bear to look. The sight of these frail and starving children brought tears to his eyes. How could it be that while millions of people were getting ready for Christmas, having parties and buying presents, these people in Africa didn't even have enough food to eat? He felt helpless and guilty at the same time.

He switched the T.V. off wiped the tear from his eye and looked out of the window. London was lit up by coloured lights, sparkling Christmas trees.

He heard laughter and singing coming from people at parties. But he couldn't get the sound of the starving children's crying out of his mind.

His thoughts were interrupted by the telephone ringing.

"George is that you?" asked the caller.

"Yes hello, who's that?" replied George.

"It's me, Bob, how are you?" said Bob, George's friend.

"I'm fine, but I've just watched the news and I was upset by the report about the famines in Ethiopia," said George hastily.

"That's why I rang," continued Bob.

"Do you want to send some money? I'll write a cheque and we can send it to charity," offered George eagerly.

"No I don't, I want your voice," replied Bob.

Bob went on to explain how he had also been horrified by the report of the famine and so, as he was a well known pop singer too, he was trying to arrange for a large group of singers and musicians to join together to make a charity record for Christmas.

"That's a great idea Bob, when do you want to do it?" asked George.

"Tomorrow," replied Bob, "meet us all at the studio tomorrow." George agreed and knew that whatever Christmas plans he had for tomorrow, would have to wait.

As George arrived at the recording studio early the next morning, he was amazed to see so many famous singers and musicians. He shook hands with lots of his friends. They all agreed that this was a great idea making a record to sell for the famine stricken people of Africa.

Nobody knew what to expect as they walked in. The musicians were already playing tunes and trying out arrangements. Bob stepped forward. "Hello everyone, thanks for coming. We've got one day to record this song so we're going to have to work hard. Let's get started."

Next, Bob sang the song through and gave everyone a copy of the words. It was arranged so that different singers would sing different lines. The song was about the suffering in Africa. At the end everyone joined together to sing the final chorus. George's part was easy but he had to sing it 2 or 3 times to get it just right.

Finally the whole song was finished and everyone sat down to hear the final version. They listened excitedly, nervous in the hope that it would sound just right. Everyone cheered, it was fantastic, the music and singing fitted together perfectly.

"Thanks everyone," shouted Bob. "You are all brilliant. Now all we've got to do is turn this tape into records and CD's and sell them." George went home tired, yet satisfied.

The next morning he heard on the news about the record they'd made. It was going to be in the shops to buy that afternoon and if as many people as possible bought a copy they could make millions of pounds for the victims of the famine in Africa.

During the next few days the record sold like hot cakes. Every record shop, supermarket, department store soon sold out. It was going to be the Christmas Number 1.

On Christmas Eve George watched the news again. Once again he saw the terrible pictures of the children in Africa sad and hungry, but he was glad that he had done something to help them.

Thought/Prayer

God of All People,

So many people in the world are starving, whilst others have plenty.

A great deal is done by charitable organisations to help the disadvantaged.

May we appreciate the good work of these charities and the donations made by others in terms of their time and money.

These are our thoughts and this is our prayer.

> **Theme:** Honesty
>
> **Introduction:**
> *This story is set in China. It emphasises the importance of being truthful.*

Many hundreds of years ago the Emperor of China was growing old.

Emperor Nang had been a wise and generous leader and he was loved by his people. But now he was elderly and quite frail. He knew himself it was time to step down and hand over to a younger man.

Unfortunately Emperor Nang had no children, no obvious heir to the throne. He decided to select the new Emperor himself.

After a great deal of thought he sent for the three most noble young men. Men who had proved themselves brave and strong.

The Emperor summoned the men to his beautiful palace near Peking. They stood before him in the Great Hall, which was hung with gorgeous tapestries set off with huge vases full of the most colourful flowers.

The young men were nervous standing before their great leader in such royal surroundings.

Nang rose slowly to his feet and spoke. "I have decided to hand over the throne to one of you fine young, noble men. I am old and it is now time for a new leader."

The three looked sideways at one another unsure whether they should smile, say something or fall on their knees before the great Emperor.

Before they could decide what to do, Emperor Nang continued, "In order to choose the right man, I set you a challenge. Each of you will have one night to fish in the palace lake. Your catch will influence my decision and will prove your skill."

With that the Emperor clapped his small hands together and large doors swung open. An army of servants marched into the hall and led the young men out of the grounds of the palace.

The three men stood in front of the lake, which was surprisingly small. The water sparkled in the sunlight and the reeds and small neat trees quivered in the gentle breeze. Although they stared into the deep clear water, the young men could see no fish.

That night the first man, Jin Han took his boat, nets, fishing rods, bait and all manner of equipment and went alone to the lake. Although he laboured all night and fished every metre of the lake, he ended the night wet and disappointed with nothing in his net but weeds and mud. He left the palace grounds without saying a word.

The following night the second contender, Li, attempted to catch something. He was an accomplished fisherman and he had been visualising the beautiful carp, angelfish, eels and others that might swim in this royal lake. But Li had no luck and like Jin Han fled the palace at dawn without a word.

Si Pin, the youngest of the men, took his turn the next night. He was worried that his two fellow challengers would have fished out all of the finest creatures. He wondered what he would discover. He waded and swam, cast his line, dragged his net but nothing appeared, not the slightest flick of a fin. Si Pin sat with his chin on his knee on the shore and watched as the sun broke across the magnificent gardens. A lily leaf beside him trembled as a frog hopped on to it from the palace lawn.

"Huh," said Si Pin, "a frog! Not exactly the catch of an Emperor."

Nevertheless Si Pin quickly captured the frog in his cupped hands and left the palace quite embarrassed.

The Emperor had arranged to view what the three men had caught the next afternoon in the Great Hall.

The room had been set with silver thrones and sitting on each were the Chinese elders, called from all parts of the Empire to discover who would be their new Master.

The three young men had cleaned themselves up and they paraded one after the other with their party of servants. Jin Han, the first stepped forward and his servant placed a magnificent wooden chest on the step in front of the Emperor. A gong sounded as the lid was lifted. A shower of crushed ice spilled out on to the marble floor. In the chest lay an enormous glistening fish. Its still round eyes flashed golden and its scales shimmered like treasure.

The Emperor said nothing but signalled to the second competitor. Li's crate was equally ornate and when the lid rose, the people gathered in the hall drew breath when they saw the massive octopus that lay before them. The Emperor's face, however, was motionless. He indicated to Si Pin to step forward.

There was an embarrassed silence as Si Pin kneeled before the great Emperor. Si Pin had nothing; no chest, no net, no offering.

"Sire," he muttered, "I caught a frog but it escaped, I beg your forgiveness, I have failed."

The crowd mumbled and pointed and the two other challengers smiled at one another.

The Emperor stood quickly and lifted his hands. The people were silenced immediately. "I have decided," he declared, looking at the men, "Si Pin, you shall be our new leader."

The gasps of shock hissed around the room but the Emperor spoke again before anything could be said. "My lake has been empty of fish for fifty years. Si Pin was the only man honest enough to admit that he had caught nothing. These other two men are not truthful and they tried to trick us. Truth and wisdom are the qualities that we need in a new leader and I trust that Si Pin will rule this land with honesty and courage."

With that Emperor Nang took Si Pin by the hand and led him up the steps to the throne. The people cheered and clapped, the bells rang and sweet smelling smoke wafted into the air.

Jin Han and Li sloped out of the room shamefaced.

Emperor Si Pin ruled wisely for many years that followed and whilst there were never any fish in the palace lake, you could occasionally see a frog hopping from lily pad to lily pad.

Thought/Prayer

God of the World,

We must remember that we will be judged by our honesty. We should never lie in order to gain something for ourselves.

Help us to be truthful in all that we think, say and do. Each one of us expects to be told the truth. May we in turn be honest with everyone around us.

These are our thoughts and this is our prayer.

An illustration for this story is to be found on page 150.

The Mask

Theme: Gifts and Talents

Introduction:
Chinedu dreams of being a member of the village drumming group in Nigeria but he really is not good enough.

In a small village in Nigeria there lived a young man named Chinedu.

Chinedu was tall and lean, he had a lovely bright wide smile.

The time was fast approaching when Chinedu could be considered an adult and he could take up his place as a full member of the community.

Chinedu loved playing the drum. He had an old djembe drum, which he loved and he longed to join the village group that played during special occasions.

Unfortunately, Chinedu wasn't very good. He had difficulty keeping in time and often his rhythms were out of step with the rest of the players.

It was full moon and the villagers were planning a special celebration. It was also Chief Mbuga's birthday and the party was planned to be glorious.

The village was made ready with garlands of flowers, feasting tables erected and large fires prepared.

"Chinedu, you must bring your drum for the party this evening. You are now old enough to join the group," announced Pato, the group leader. Chinedu was thrilled. He vowed to try his very best and prove himself.

The celebrations soon began. Chinedu took his place in the group sitting next to large torches, which blazed with the same excitement as the party-goers. Chinedu felt the pulse of the drums thumping in his ears and he began beating his djembe. But, true to form, he was awkward and irregular. His playing contrasted with the steady thump of the others and soon the music was stopped by Pato.

"Chinedu, keep in time!" called the leader. But it was no use, for as soon as Chinedu began again, he was equally clumsy and out of time.

Chief Mbuga came across and called to Pato, "Pato what's happening man, why are you stopping and starting?"

"I'm sorry Chief, we'll keep on playing," Pato replied humbly and then turned to Chinedu and quietly instructed him. "Chinedu, please sit out, I'm afraid I can't let you play."

Chinedu was sad and embarrassed as he walked back to his hut, pulling his djembe drum behind him.

Chinedu's sister found him sitting in darkness, whilst the rest of the village partied. She asked him what was wrong, he was usually so bright and happy. Chinedu tearfully explained to his sister about his poor drumming and how he longed to be better and play in the group.

"You should visit the mask maker Chinedu," she declared after a little while, "explain to her and ask her for a mask."

Chinedu did not really understand how the mask maker could solve his musical problem, but early the next morning Chinedu walked out of the village towards the river. He crossed the water, travelled through the long grass and came to a small hut, which nestled in a crater. The door was open. Chinedu held his breath as he entered. All around the walls of the hut were strange and beautiful masks. They were made from bark, animal skins and wood. They were painted in bold colours. Their patterns and features were a feast for the eyes.

From the back of the room a small, happy looking old lady stepped forward. "Can I help you Chinedu?" she breathed.

Chinedu was surprised that she knew his name. He slowly told his story and asked the old woman if she had a mask that would help him with the skills that he so desperately wanted. The mask maker did not hesitate. She reached up to the left hand wall and pulled down a large orange and black mask with extreme features.

She handed it to Chinedu and announced. "Wear this."

The room darkened and she was gone. Chinedu turned the mask in his hands and felt a little frightened. He quickly ran out of the hut and kept on running until he was in sight of his village.

That evening the drummers were to play again. The fires were lit and the villagers gathered with food and drink to enjoy the party atmosphere as it continued.

Secretly, in his hut Chinedu put on the mask. He quivered a little and then reached for his drum. He strode out and confidently walked over to the drummers. He sat in position and began drumming along. His forearms, wrists and fingers felt full of power and certainty.

His drumming was superb. He was rhythmic and inventive. Very soon the other drummers were quiet as they were in awe of this masked drummer and his supernatural beat. When the music finished Pato respectfully enquired who was behind the mask. Gasps of shock and surprise hissed through the group as Chinedu revealed himself.

"Chinedu it's you, you're... you're a great drummer!" Pato didn't know what to say.

From then on Chinedu was the main feature of the drumming group. He led new beat patterns and drove the music along with gusto. All manner of villagers would start dancing when they heard Chinedu. His rhythms were infectious. However he only achieved this when he wore the mask. It was as if the mask provided him with this amazing skill.

But tragedy was soon to strike, for as Chinedu was returning from another festival in a nearby village he had to cross a large swollen river.

He struggled to hold both his djembe and his mask above his head. He stumbled on a rock in the water and let go of the mask. It was taken by the quick current of the river and was soon engulfed and lost. Chinedu half swam, half scrambled to the shore and squelched down to the ground. His mask was gone, was his drumming ability gone too?

Chinedu was nervous as he sat with the group. They looked at his face. He knew what they were thinking. The beat started and the worst had happened, Chinedu could not drum. He was hopeless. All of the wonderful music had disappeared from his hands, floated away like the mask on the river.

Chinedu stood up, picked up his drum and marched resolutely to the river. He lifted his faithful old drum above his head and with all his strength threw it into the centre of the river.

He turned without looking to see if the drum was floating and ran back to the village, tears burning at his cheeks.

For many days Chinedu spoke to no one. Even his kind sister could not coax him from his distress.

However, Chinedu was essentially a happy young man and he couldn't maintain his depression for very long. One sunny afternoon he came and sat by his sister who was painting animal scenes on large boards for the village school. Chinedu watched and then quickly picked up a paintbrush.

"Lions don't look like that ," he declared to his sister. He then quickly applied the paint to the board. His hand moved gracefully and with great confidence.

"Chinedu that's superb, I didn't know you could paint," she said surprised when she looked at his picture.

"Er I can't or, well, I don't," he said equally surprised.

"Paint me a spoonbill," his sister commanded.

Chinedu obediently picked up another brush, loaded it with white paint and formed the perfect body of the large bird.

"There," he said smiling, "a spoonbill."

"Chinedu you are an artist, a fantastic artist," his sister shouted with glee.

She quickly rushed and obtained more paint, brushes and boards. Everything she asked for, Chinedu painted beautifully. He amazed himself. "Where did I learn this?" he pondered not knowing that he had the ability.

Later in the week Chief Mbuga was standing looking at the wonderful mural that Chinedu was engaged in painting. The Chief coughed to get the young man's attention and then spoke. "Chinedu, you may not be much of a drummer, but man can you paint!"

Chinedu lifted his head and held his brush in the air.

"Thank you Chief," he said and let out a yell of happiness.

Thought/Prayer

God of the World,

We all have ambitions, we would like to achieve great things. Often we are successful in using our talents well. However, sometimes we are not able to be as good as we would like to be at certain things. Yet everyone has gifts, everyone is skilful at something.

May we try to make the best of our gifts and appreciate our natural ability.

These are our thoughts and this is our prayer.

An illustration for this story is to be found on page 151.

Ryan Meets a Celebrity

> **Theme:** The Sermon on the Mount
>
> **Introduction:**
> *Ryan's attitude towards the way he lives his life changes when his father takes him to listen to a famous person who delivers some powerful words.*
>
> (The extract is taken from St Matthew's Gospel 5:3-10)

Ryan was always boasting. He constantly declared that everything he did was better, bigger, faster than anyone else. "I can throw stones further than any other child in the village," he would trumpet. "My dad has the finest sheep on the hillside," he would claim.

Eventually most of the boys and girls in their village avoided him. They got fed up of his showing off. Samuel, who had the same birthday as Ryan remained loyal and put up with Ryan's over-inflated stories just for the sake of their friendship.

One morning Ryan's dad told him that they were going that afternoon to see a special person, a local celebrity.

"Wow," hissed Ryan and rushed out to find Sam.

"Who could it be?" considered Ryan. Maybe a Roman General a famous warrior, a wealthy vineyard owner.

When he found Sam he ran up to him practically knocking him over in his eagerness. "My dad's taking me to see a star – a soldier, a king, a rich man . . . he'll probably show me his sword, maybe he'll give me money or let me ride in his carriage." Ryan didn't stop to breathe as he spoke. He gave a high excited shriek, punched Sam on the shoulder, and ran back home.

"Come on Ryan, let's go," called the boy's father. They walked out of the village and off in the direction of Jerusalem. After a few miles they reached a long low flat plain that rose slightly at the edge. A crowd had gathered. "Where is he, where is the army?" stuttered Ryan searching for the glistening of armour, gold or anything which indicated fame and fortune. "Just watch and listen," said his dad calmly.

A man stood up in front of the crowd. He was wearing a sandy coloured tunic. His longish hair fell to his shoulders. As he began to speak the crowd hushed. 'He's not a famous person, he's no soldier, superstar, what's this all about?' thought Ryan with disappointment and frustration.

"Just listen,' breathed his dad.

The man spoke,
"Blessed are the poor in spirit: for theirs is the kingdom of heaven.
Blessed are they who mourn: for they shall be comforted.
Blessed are the meek: for they shall inherit the earth.
Blessed are they who hunger and thirst for righteousness: for they shall be filled.
Blessed are the merciful: for they shall obtain mercy.
Blessed are the pure in heart: for they shall see God.
Blessed are the peacemakers for they shall be called the children of God.
Blessed are they who are persecuted for righteousness' sake for theirs is the kingdom of heaven."

As the words filtered out across the crowd, their impact was amazing. It was as if some warm healing breeze was soothing a pain. Ryan considered the words.

'Humble,' he thought, 'meek.' He cast his mind back to how he'd harassed Samuel. He felt guilty.

"Who is that man Dad?" asked Ryan, looking up at his father.

"That's Jesus, the special person I told you about," he replied.

The words that Jesus had spoken were floating through Ryan's mind. The words had touched his heart. Ryan was certainly not meek, he knew inside that he had lost friends because of his boasting and showing off.

Ryan looked around at other people in the crowd. People were chatting quietly, sharing their thoughts. Ryan could see clearly that they were moved.

"Time to go," said his dad.

"Wait Dad," he replied. Ryan stood up and walked up to the mount where Jesus was now sitting listening to the people around him.

"Jesus," Ryan spoke quietly, "Jesus." The man turned and looked. "Jesus what you said. . . I . . . er . . . " Ryan stumbled over his words, "er . . . thank you, thank you very much."

Ryan held out his hand, which Jesus clasped briefly. He smiled, opening his brown eyes wide. Ryan smiled in return and then went back to his dad.

On their way home Ryan was quiet. Just before they reached their small village he said to his dad. "I've been showing off a lot recently, I think I'm going to change."

Ryan's dad said nothing, he just put his hand on his son's shoulder and led him home.

Thought/Prayer

God of the World,

May we be peacemakers.

May we be humble and merciful.

Let us be gentle and try to do the right thing and may we be gentle in all our dealings with other people.

In this way we can live our lives in a truthful and honest way and be free of anxiety.

These are our thoughts and this is our prayer.

> **Theme:** Each Person is Special
>
> **Introduction:**
> *This story is set in France. When a Prince becomes the new ruler he discovers that his kingdom has not been run with justice or equality.*

In a large and stunningly beautiful chateau in France there lived a Prince. He was wealthy, the richest man in the land. He was also sad. The sadness he felt was because his father, the king, had recently died leaving him to rule. His father had been so strong and confident. He had had many friends and always enjoyed lavish banquets and hunting parties. The Prince however had no friends. He had no one except the ministers who attended to the king and advised him.

To be truthful, the Prince did not trust these ministers. There was something false about their smiles, something greedy about the way they dressed and used the royal money to buy themselves the most lavish gifts.

One clear spring morning the Prince was sitting high up in the castle tower looking out over Quimper, the nearby town. He could only recall visiting Quimper once or twice in his life and that was in a magnificent royal procession alongside his father.

"I should visit Quimper again and see my people," he considered to himself.

Immediately he ran down the steps to the minister's chamber burst in and said to the Prime Minister. "Could you arrange for me to visit Quimper tomorrow Prime Minister, I wish to visit my people."

The Prime Minister looked a little startled and replied uncertainly. "I can arrange a visit Sire, but not for tomorrow. The preparations take several weeks for a royal visit."

"I see," replied the Prince suspiciously, "then make arrangements for a visit as soon as possible and notify me of the date."

The Prince left the Prime Minister's chamber and walked back up the many steps to the tower, thinking hard.

Little did the Prince know that the ordinary townspeople of Quimper were very poor and deprived. The Prince's father and the ministers were cruel rulers, taxing the people heavily and using the wealth of the people for a luxurious life.

Whenever a royal visit had taken place it had avoided the poorest parts of the town. Only certain townspeople had been allowed to greet the royal procession.

Only certain buildings had been decorated with flowers and painted to give the impression that all was well in the town. In fact many things were wrong, very wrong. The poverty had led to dishonesty, violence and cruelty. Many families lived meagre lives fearing what might befall them. And still the royal family demanded taxes and used their soldiers to enforce their greedy tax laws.

As the Prince climbed the stairs he made a plan. In the early hours of the next morning the prince carefully put on some poor and tattered clothes to disguise himself and quietly crept out of the chateau using the back door from the kitchen.

Nobody saw him as he walked determinedly to the town. The sun was just rising and beams of sunlight magically penetrated the narrow streets, lighting them so that the Prince could glimpse the scene.

What met his eyes shocked him. The houses were shabby, bad smells pervaded the air. Skinny dogs and goats roamed the streets sniffing at rubbish, which lay on the ground.

A shutter opened and a small child with sunken eyes looked out at the Prince. He turned and greeted the child kindly, but the young girl looked afraid and turned back shouting for her mother.

The door burst open and a ragged looking woman ran out brandishing a stick. She hit the Prince hard on the shoulder and gruffly told him to be off.

The Prince was hurt and shocked. He turned to reprimand the woman, but as their eyes met he knew that she was more afraid than he was. She had the look of a wounded animal protecting her young. The Prince said nothing and walked on through the miserable streets rubbing his bruised shoulder.

As the day progressed the Prince was stunned by the poverty, fear and degradation amongst the people. 'How can my people live like this? What did my father think? What has gone wrong?' these questions raced around his mind. No one had recognised him all day and he finally decided to return to the castle and ask the Prime Minister some searching questions.

He once again chose the kitchen door to return into his castle. As he approached he saw a young servant girl whom he recognised. She had served him his meal occasionally. She looked at him and then looked again realising that this scruffily dressed man was in fact her master. She knelt low. "Sire," she began and then stopped not knowing what to say next.

"Tell me this," the Prince asked decisively, "do you live in Quimper?"

"Yes Sire," she replied.

"And is it a poor town with a great deal of poverty and crime?"

The servant hesitated looking afraid.

"You can tell me," continued the Prince gently.

"Well yes Sire, but I am grateful for my work here at the castle. I share my wages with my family, my father is ill and my mother . . . "

"I understand," interrupted the Prince.

Now he realised how things were. He looked again at the girl.

"But why did my father allow such poverty, did he not help his people?"

An angry look flashed across the servant's eyes. "Your father increased the taxes, demanded more and more from the people, commanded his soldiers to deal cruelly with all who would not pay. My uncle . . . " she stopped and looked both embarrassed and afraid.

"Do not worry, things will change," retorted the Prince.

He said goodbye to the servant and strode up into the castle. He burst into the Prime Minister's chamber and knocked over a small table of fine wine and cheese as he confronted the man.

"THIS IS A DISGRACE!" he shouted, "that my people should live in poverty and fear whilst we drink expensive wine up here in the castle." He did not give the Prime Minister a chance to reply. "There is no care, friendship, kindness or consideration amongst the people. Their lives are sinking. The children are not growing up as they should. Something must be done and I am starting with you. You are dismissed," the Prince was now looking powerful and regal.

"But Sire, I serve you dutifully, please understand the situation," replied the Prime Minister in an uncertain voice.

"I understand full well. Guards!" he shouted to the soldiers outside the door. "Take the Prime Minister and throw him out of the castle."

The guards would not disobey a royal command so they gathered the terrified minister up by his arms and dragged him out of the chateau.

That day the Prince summoned all of the servants and cooks from the kitchen and appointed them as his new ministers. Together they discussed how they would improve the lives of the people in the town.

They started cleaning up the streets, providing decent food for families, dealing with crime, establishing schools for the children. The greedy tax laws were abolished and the rich houses of the ministers were turned into hospitals and libraries. The Prince opened up the massive grounds of the castle as a park for the people to enjoy. They worked together. It was tiring work. At times they felt exhausted, but slowly life began to improve.

As the quality of life became better, a new spirit grew amongst the people. New friends were made, people began to help one another again, the children grew up well, learning to be friends with one another, learning and growing as skillful people.

A year later as the Prince was standing high up in the castle looking out over the town, his new Prime Minister, the girl who had been the servant from the kitchen, turned to him and said, "You have brought life, love and friendship back to this town, now it will grow and be good."

The Prince smiled, his heart felt warm as the sun set over the beautiful town of Quimper.

Thought/Prayer

God of Equality and Justice,

Each person is special. Everyone is born equal and should be treated with equal respect. Unfortunately many people live in very different circumstances. Some communities are very poor and disadvantaged whilst others are wealthy and privileged.

May justice and fairness sweep across the world and leaders with influence encourage harmony and respect for all.

These are our thoughts and this is our prayer.

Theme: Somebody Looks After Us

Introduction:
This story is set in Switzerland. It is about Gemma and her father who are skillful mountain climbers. As she grows up, Gemma wants to climb higher and faster, but she needs someone to watch out for her.

Gemma and her dad lived in a beautiful mountainous part of Switzerland. Gemma's dad was an experienced mountain climber. If you stood and looked out of Gemma's bedroom window, every mountain peak that you could see had been climbed by Gemma's dad.

As a small child Gemma would spend hours in her dad's kit room in the basement of the house. In this room was a collection of colourful ropes, shining metal clasps, pins and pegs, specialised jackets and shoes hung from the walls and all manner of camping equipment sat on large shelves. As she played on the floor she watched her dad check and clean the equipment.

"You have to look after your kit Gem," he would say, "safety first!"

Occasionally Gemma would pull a rope from a loop and tie it around her arms and legs. Very often she would stumble in a tangled knot of cord like a baby spider learning how to weave a web. Gemma's dad would smile and gently and patiently untangle his daughter and carefully rehang the rope.

On the morning of her ninth birthday Gemma's dad handed her a medium sized rectangular present. Gemma eagerly pulled off the paper, opened the box and took out a pair of climbing shoes.

"Size 1 just right for you darling," smiled her father.

"You mean we're going climbing dad?" Gemma squeaked.

"Nine years old, big enough for your first expedition," said her dad with pride.

Later that day father and daughter strode out towards the gentle slope of the nearest hill. Gemma's dad showed his daughter how to reach and pull. Where best to place your foot on the rock face. The method for letting the rope out as you climbed and how to hammer in the metal clasps that secured the rope to the rock. Although they barely climbed as high as their house Gemma's dad could see that his little girl was a natural.

The orange sun was fading in dusty beams as they looked across to the highest peak. Gemma pointed at it and asked her dad what it was called.

"That mountain is called 'To the Moon'," he said, "it's the highest peak in this region. It gets its name from its tremendous height and difficulty. Look," he continued, "the moon is sitting on its summit." Sure enough the yellow moon looked as if it was perched on the very top of the mountain.

"One day," breathed Gemma, "I'm going 'To the Moon'." Gemma's dad said nothing. He took his child's hand and walked her home.

Nine turned to ten and the years passed quickly for Gemma. She was a super mountaineer. She was nimble, had great balance and powerful strength in her shoulders. A line of trophies soon adorned the shelves in their house.

Gemma and her dad often climbed together. He taught her everything he knew. As she went higher and faster he found that he had to work harder to keep up. Some days Gemma would stumble and trip. Her dad's strong hand was always there to catch her and hold her safe on the mountainside.

When Gemma was seventeen she approached her dad tentatively and said, "Dad I want to climb 'To the Moon'."

Her father looked doubtful. "I'm sorry love you are not ready. It's so high and sheer. You need more experience first."

"I am ready!" she shouted, "I'm not a child anymore, I can do it!"

"Not yet Gemma," he replied firmly.

Gemma's face was fixed with anger, her lips tight and her shoulders pulled up. She turned her back and marched out of the room.

The next morning, while it was still dark, Gemma silently got out of bed. She reached into her cupboard where she had concealed her climbing gear. Lifting the pack onto her back she crept out of the house. The air was still and icy, she could taste the chill of the atmosphere between her teeth. After driving her father's four-wheel drive for an hour she reached the foot of 'To the Moon'. The sun was rising and she looked up at the towering mountain as the light broke across its awesome rock faces.

Gemma began steadily and strong. Handling her ropes and climbing pegs skillfully. The higher she climbed the more remote she felt. The mist seemed to blow in around her feet and she could no longer see the ground below. The day had seemed promising, but it was obvious that there was a climate change in the air.

Gemma was determined and climbed even quicker. But her eagerness meant that the climbing clasps that held the ropes were not being hammered in to the rock as securely as was necessary.

Gemma reached an overhang that jutted out above her head, blocking out the sun. It looked impossible to climb. But there was no going back. She reached, twisted, and strained every sinew of her muscles. She felt the bite of the rock on her fingers as she struggled to climb.

Suddenly her grip broke and she fell. Like a game bird shot in flight she plummeted. As she fell the clasp that should have held her rope popped out of the rock. Gemma tried to get a hold but the momentum was too great and she plunged into the mist below her.

'I'm going to die,' she thought terrified. "Dad," she gasped.

All at once she felt the rope pull tight and her descent stopped, her body bounced. A hand reached out to her from the mist and pulled her on to the ledge.

Gemma slumped into her dad's arms. He held her tight and quietly said, "You're safe Gemma, I'm here."

Gemma's heart raced, her breath panted and her eyes streamed. She couldn't speak but there was a question bursting in her eyes.

Her dad spoke quietly, "I followed you Gem. You couldn't see me but I was always there, climbing just below you. I couldn't let you go on your own."

Gemma felt ashamed, but she was safe, secure in her father's care. After a few moments he said, "Come on love, we're going 'To the Moon'."

When the two of them had mustered their strength they began the final ascent. Gemma's dad helped her past the overhang and within an hour father and daughter stood triumphant at the top. The mist had cleared and the sun set warm across the land. Above their heads the golden moon rose and bathed the mountain in grey silver light.

Gemma took her father's hand and looked up at him, "Thank you for taking me 'To the Moon' Dad," she whispered gratefully.

Thought/Prayer

God of the High Mountains and Deep Valleys,

Throughout our lives people look after us. Often we are not even aware of their presence and care. Sometimes we take for granted those who watch over us and keep us safe.

May we be grateful for the kindness and care we receive from those who love and look after us as part of their daily lives.

We think especially of the many people who work in caring services, who are committed and skillful and provide support and care everyday for many people in need.

These are our thoughts and this is our prayer.

The Peace Dove

Theme: Peace

Introduction:
Through their sharing and play, two boys are able to heal the scars of war between their two communities. This story is set in The Middle East.

In a troubled part of the world in the Middle East two young boys lived. Jerome lived with his mother, his father had died, in fact his father had been killed in the fighting. There was fighting everyday there. Soldiers, bombs, shooting. Each morning Jerome and his mother would awaken to the sound of gunfire.

The other boy, Saeed, lived a mile away with his brothers, sisters, his mother and father. In between Jerome and Saeed's homes was the wasteland known as No-man's Land. Nobody would cross this land, it was broken up by bombs and shells. Any houses that had been built there had long been destroyed.

Jerome's people were Israelis, whilst Saeed's were Palestinian and it seemed like the fighting between these two groups of people had been going on forever and would never end.

"Never cross the wasteland," Jerome's mother would say, "you make sure you never go near the Palestinian homes."

"Yes Mother," replied Jerome. 'But why were they fighting?' he wondered. He didn't know and nobody ever explained. Of course he was sad about his father's death, he was heartbroken. But what was the reason?

Saeed's family had given him the same warning also. "Those Israelis are dangerous, they want to force us out. Have nothing to do with them," Saeed's family declared.

Jerome loved football. He used to watch all the international matches on satellite T.V. He knew about David Beckham, Ruud van Nilstelrooy, Ryan Giggs – even though he lived thousands of miles away. He would take his ball and kick it against a large wall just in front of the wasteland.

One morning in April, he was practising when he let go with a most powerful shot. The ball travelled like one of the shells from the artillery guns. Over the wall and out onto the wasteland it flew. Jerome looked around, nobody was present, so he quickly ran out to retrieve it.

At first he couldn't find it amongst the ruined houses and battered, burnt out cars. Eventually he spied it lodged between two fallen trees.

He kicked and dribbled the ball. He mooched around the wasteland, looking at all the objects and abandoned household items. Suddenly, he stopped dead. His heart raced in his mouth and his eyes watered. From behind the shell of a car, a figure had appeared and was looking at him.

"I'm going to be killed," thought Jerome panicking. But then he realised that it was a boy the same age as him. It was Saeed, who had also wandered onto the wasteland.

As Jerome looked more closely, he noticed that Saeed was wearing something that he recognised. It was a Manchester United football shirt. This made Jerome smile. And Saeed smiled back. Slowly but very accurately without a word, Jerome passed the ball to Saeed and Saeed chipped it back.

Kick, kick, backwards and forwards, they played it between them. Then Jerome made a goal with two empty oilcans. The game continued. The boys laughed, but never spoke. Their languages were different, but they used the international languages of friendship and football.

Each day, the boys would cautiously come out on to the wasteland to meet up and play football. They enjoyed each other's company. They found that they were alike in so many ways.

One day, as Jerome was bending down to lift the ball, he noticed something white and twitching. It was a dove, clearly it had been injured and it trembled with pain and fear. Jerome lifted it gently and cupped it in his hands. Saeed came across and looked. He smoothed its feathers gently with the back of his hand.

The boys quickly and carefully ran back towards Jerome's house and found a box in his shed. They made a bed for the damaged dove and fed it seeds and insects.

Each day, after football, the boys crouched in Jerome's shed and nursed the bird. The dove grew stronger and began to flap around the shed. Then late one afternoon, Jerome's mother came looking for him. When she saw him together with Saeed she shouted, "What are you doing here with him!?" she pointed to Saeed. "He's a Palestinian and you know we hate the Palestinians."

"He's my friend mother. He's my good friend," replied Jerome.

"Get out, Get out!" she cried and moved towards Saeed with menace. Saeed ran fearfully back across the wasteland.

That evening Jerome's grandmother came to visit. She found Jerome and his mother in tears. Jerome explained to his granny that his mum had said he must never see Saeed again. He also showed her the dove that the two boys had nursed back to health and was now flying around the garden.

Jerome's mother felt bad, but she hated the Palestinians for what they had done.

Early next morning, Jerome and his mother awoke. It was different, for the first time in weeks there was no gunfire or shouting. They heard a different sound coming from the garden. They could hear the warbling and cooing of the dove.

"What a beautiful sound," Jerome's mother thought. And then she said to herself, "I have been wrong. My child Jerome has found a friend, a boy just like him. These boys are our future – I must let them build their friendship."

After breakfast, Jerome's mother came into the kitchen carrying the football.

"Jerome," she said, "here, take the ball and go and find Saeed and play football. Tell him the dove is singing and tell him that I am sorry."

Jerome looked up at his mother, smiled, then quickly snatched the ball and ran across the wasteland to find his friend.

Thought/Prayer

God of Peace,

Many communities are torn apart by fighting. Often the reason for their conflict has long been forgotten. In most cases the ordinary people suffer because of the war.

May the hand of peace touch these troubled places and people.

May the children provide the peace in the future as they grow and learn tolerance and respect for all other members of the global family.

These are our thoughts and this is our prayer.

An illustration for this story is to be found on page 152.

> **Theme:** Making Choices/Health
>
> Introduction:
> *This story is set in Nigeria. It tells of how some young girls have to make decisions about what they eat.*
>
> *The story may prompt thoughts about drug abuse.*

In the centre of Africa at the edge of The Kalahari Desert the Ampoosu Tribe lived in a small village. They were good people who lived a happy life and managed to exist in harmony with their surroundings.

For three quarters of the year there was enough food for the Ampoosu. They grew potatoes and sweet beans. They hunted for small animals and birds. They made pan bread and drank the juice of the fruits that grew in the bushes around their village. Water in the well was clean and in good supply. However, for three months of the year in the dry season, life was much harder.

This was the time when the sun burnt the soil, dried up the well, withered the plants and sent any wildlife on a journey North in search of water. The Ampoosu people planned for the dry season. They stored up food, kept supplies of water and juice in large jars in the shade of the trees. But there was no escaping it, they ate much less, always felt hungry and tasted the dry sand in their mouths for much of the day.

Adupe was a young Ampoosu girl who lived with her mother and brother in the village. She hated the dry season. She was uncomfortable with the ache of hunger in her tummy. She rolled her tongue across her teeth imagining the cool water from the well and the sweet juice of the berries that she ate in the good seasons.

Adupe had two friends who lived in the next village. Karla and Manny would often visit Adupe and they would walk out in the forest together. Their favourite games were skipping and stone throwing. Adupe was a fantastic thrower, she could send a stone flying high over the trees. She could hit the centre of a tree stump from twenty or thirty metres. Karla and Manny skipped forwards, backwards, at double speed, whilst running and singing all manner of songs and rhymes. The girls had great fun together. But in the dry season they were hungry and thirsty and it was hard to find the enthusiasm to play their games together.

One particularly hot and dry day Manny and Karla ran into the Ampoosu village excited and lively.

"Adupe," they shouted, "we have found a fruit bush, full of lovely, juicy fruits. They are not completely ripe yet, but any day now."

Adupe was surprised to hear of any fruit bush growing in the dry season and she asked her friends to describe the bush, the leaves and the fruits themselves. As the girls told her about the long thin leaves and the deep purple colour of the fruit, Adupe started to worry. Her grandmother had told her about a rare bush called the Mindu Plant that grew all year round, produced delicious fruits but actually was very bad for you. Adupe's grandmother had warned her never to eat from the Mindu plant, for although it might satisfy you at first it would cause you harm.

Adupe said nothing but followed her friend as they led her into a part of the forest that they had never visited before. The shadows grew longer and the smell of the earth changed. After what seemed like a long walk, the girls came upon a large spindly looking bush. Its leaves were slender like arrow heads and the purple fruit hung heavy, with a sticky gleaming skin that caught the rays of sunshine that broke through the forest canopy.

"This might be the Mindu Plant," Adupe said uncertainly, "I'm not sure if we should eat these fruits."

"Aren't you hungry, wouldn't you like to taste some sweet juice? There won't be anything other than dry beans for a whole month, come on Adupe try one," insisted Karla.

Manny and Karla plucked a purple fruit from the bush and bit into the sticky skin. Immediately clear juice dripped from their lips, their eyes lit up and they began to eat greedily. They picked another and another, shovelling the food into their mouths with great delight.

Adupe reached her hand forward and felt the fruit in her fingers. She was so hungry, she could smell the juice. She tugged and the purple food fell into her hand. She faltered and then sunk her teeth into the flesh of the fruit. The taste was wonderful. Her mouth tingled with the taste, her tummy jumped as the hunger that she had known for weeks began to subside.

The three girls enjoyed the feast for several minutes and then lay down in the sunshine feeling totally satisfied.

When they stood up to go back to the village they felt dizzy. Their heads were spinning and the satisfied feeling in their stomach was turning into a low throbbing pain.

"I don't feel well," complained Manny.

"My head hurts and my tummy aches," continued Karla in a groggy voice.

Adupe said nothing. She knew they had eaten from the Mindu Plant and felt both ill and ashamed.

That night all three girls felt worse than they had ever felt before in their lives. They thrashed about in their beds, they were doubled up with pain in their stomachs and their heads were in a frightening spin.

However, when they woke the next day the illness had passed. The pains had gone and their tummies had settled down.

The three girls met later and spoke of their illness. They decided never to eat from the Mindu Plant again.

But only a few days later the girls were feeling empty and thirsty again.

"Let's go to the bush again," said Karla.

"I'm not sure," said Manny, "we were so ill after we'd eaten the fruit last time."

After some discussion and because the hunger was so powerful the three girls decided to go back to the Mindu Plant again.

On the way Adupe picked up a stone. She launched it in to the air but her throw was pathetic. Her arms seemed to have no strength or skill. She lifted another stone and aimed for the Honey Tree Stump a few metres away. She missed hopelessly. What was the matter? She was the champion stone thrower!

Was it the affect of the Mindu fruit? Her grandmother had warned her of the harm it could do.

As the girls approached the bush, Adupe was worried, she had to choose. She was so hungry, the juice of the fruit was so satisfying, but what had happened to her? She was worried about the illness that had followed their feast. She was so tempted, but so frightened. And her friends, what would they say if she said she wouldn't eat the fruit?

Manny reached out her hand to the fruit and pulled one. Karla did the same.

"Go on Adupe pick one," they urged.

Adupe trembled.

"No!" she announced, "it's not good for us."

"But aren't you hungry? They taste so good," replied the girls.

Adupe's stomach turned with both hunger and fear.

But she was determined.

"No!" she declared and quickly turned to walk away. She didn't want to see her friends eat the fruit, she was scared of the effect it would have on them. As she walked back towards the village through the forest she heard the sound of running feet padding behind her. She turned to see Manny and Karla chasing after her.

"What are you doing?' Adupe asked. "Have you eaten the Mindu fruit?"

"We didn't," declared her friends, "you were right, we were sick when we ate it and I've felt so weak since the last time," continued Manny.

Adupe was pleased and took a hand of each of her friends in her hands.

The three girls returned to the village and cooked up some beans and ate a decent meal together.

It wasn't long before the sound of the rain could be heard falling on the roofs of the houses in the village. The well soon refilled and food grew. The dry season had passed and everyone had plenty to eat.

Adupe and her friends felt pleased with themselves that they had been strong enough to make the right choice.

Later that year some of the elders of the tribe announced that they had found a Mindu Bush on the outskirts of the forest and they had chopped it down.

"The Mindu Plant would eventually bring sickness and even death to our people," the chief elder announced. "If anyone continues to eat its fruit it would cause terrible harm, even though its taste is sweet."

When Adupe heard this she shivered and was thankful.

Thought/Prayer

God of the World,

May we have the strength to make good choices about what we try. Even though we are tempted sometimes we must do our best to be strong and look after ourselves.

We think especially of all of the young people who have fallen ill or into sad lives because they have become addicted to drugs. May they with the help of others have a healthy future.

These are our thoughts and this is our prayer.

An illustration for this story is to be found on page 153.

> **Theme:** Deep in the Ocean
>
> **Introduction:**
> *An experienced diver makes an amazing discovery.*

The sun came up and sparkled across the ocean. There was just a hint of a breeze and the water lapped gently against the boat.

Jimmy Davidson checked his belt, tested the air in his tank and prepared to dive. This was going to be the last dive of the season for Jimmy. Perhaps his last dive ever. He had been thinking about giving up. He was getting on in age and he wasn't sure if he was still enthusiastic enough to plunge deep into the sometimes dangerous waters.

He stepped forward to the edge of the boat deck and looked down into the clear blue water. He could make out the frosty bone like coral, some lush, long seaweed leaves and the occasional tropical fish.

"Here we go," he thought and leapt.

Whoosh! – the cool, bubbling water engulfed his straight body as he fired into the depths. He sank quickly at first and then slowed and floated into a horizontal swimming position.

He took a deep, slightly stuttering breath from his air tank and then felt the magical sensation of weightlessness under the sea. A beautiful calm came over Jimmy, his body went limp and he allowed his eyes to feast on his underwater surroundings.

Tiny, orange and red fish flickered past him in silent shoals. Large manta-rays swooped above his head like prehistoric birds. The coral glinted in the sunlight that pierced the clear water in shafts. An octopus unfolded itself and moved along the sea bed like a plasticine animation. A small shark with a pointed and suspicious expression glided in a straight and determined path two metres away.

'No,' thought Jimmy, 'this is not my last dive, this is too wonderful to give up.' This always happened, as soon as Jimmy Davidson got below the surface he felt enchanted, a visitor to another world, a guest in heaven.

Jimmy unbuckled his camera from his belt and began taking photographs. The light was good and he was able to get spectacular close ups of enormous pipe fish, eels and tiger fish. He knew the name and image of every creature and every feature under the sea.

As he looked up and down he saw a string of bubbles rising from below a clump of seaweed on the sea bed. Jimmy kicked and dived down, flippers pushing him deeper. He lifted the seaweed and to his surprise he found the opening to a cave. Jimmy flicked on his powerful neon underwater torch and sent a beam of silver light into its opening. The light reached a very deep cavern indeed.

Jimmy felt a little nervous at first, he hesitated, unsure as to whether he should descend. But without another thought he plunged into the darkness. He shone his torch light around the cave and marvelled at the vivid colours of the sea plants.

As he searched, the light flashed across the knobbly back of a long grey slow moving fish. Jimmy cast the light across it again.

'What is it?' he thought. 'An eel, no, a sea pike, it can't be.' This creature had a long sloping head, thin jaws, paddle shaped flippers. 'No,' pondered Jimmy, 'It couldn't possibly be.' He realised that he recognised its shape. 'It's an Ichthyosaur.'

He had seen a picture of one in his reference books. An Ichthyosaur was a prehistoric sea dinosaur that lived 40 million years ago. Like all dinosaurs it was extinct – or so Jimmy had thought.

The long creature turned again and swam towards the diver. Jimmy glided behind a large rock and lifted his camera. As the stunning Ichthyosaur floated by, Jimmy pressed the shutter of his camera and took several photos.

The flash of the camera obviously disturbed the dinosaur, it suddenly accelerated, dipped its head and shot down into the darkness of the depths of the cave.

Jimmy was trembling, he could feel his breathing labouring from excitement and fear combined. He checked his air gauge and realised he must return to the surface.

Back in his office he plugged his camera into his laptop computer and brought up the image. There it was – a real living fish dinosaur staring out at him from his computer screen.

With a sick, thrilled feeling in his stomach he lifted the phone and dialled the number of the marine studies department of the university.

"Dr Gregson," he breathed, "it's Jimmy Davidson, I've got some photos from my dive I want to send you."

"What sort of photos Jim?" asked the professor.

"I'll send them by e-mail, now just look at them, you'll never believe it." He put down the phone and pressed send on the keyboard.

Within half an hour Dr Gregson was banging on Jimmy's door. Jimmy opened the door and saw his friend the professor followed by hoards of other people. Reporters, photographers, students.

"Jimmy," cried the professor, "how, when, where? These are unbelievable – an Ichthyosaur." The professor waved the photos in the air.

"I know," replied Jimmy, "I can't take it in myself, I dived down into a cave and there it was just a few metres away."

The professor bundled Jimmy into a room. "Now Jim you must show us in the morning where you dived, the exact spot. I've got a team of scientists, archaeologists, and natural history divers all ready to go. This is the greatest sensation in the history of marine studies."

Jimmy Davidson suddenly stopped and stared at the professor. He knew if he showed other people where he found the Ichthyosaur there would be hundreds of divers, boats, journalists, submarines, all scrabbling for a chance to see this creature that had survived for millions of years.

"No," declared Jim with a fixed look in his eye. "I'm afraid I can't show you where."

"What?" choked the professor unbelieving.

"Dr Gregson," continued Jimmy, "if I show you, the beauty, calm, solitude and wonder of that part of the ocean, can you guarantee it won't be destroyed? The Ichthyosaur lives, allow it to continue living. We must respect its rights, its environment. It's there and it is fine. That should be enough. Jimmy stopped and would not say another word. The professor opened the door to the waiting journalists. Flash lights burst and reporters moved forward.

"I'm very sorry to disappoint you ladies and gentlemen but there will be no interviews today."

Somewhere deep in the ocean the Ichthyosaur flapped its large flippers and drifted deep into a cave, secret again for another million years.

Thought/Prayer

God of the Deep Oceans and High Mountains,

We cannot possibly know what is present in the furthest reaches of our planet, under the sea, deep in the forest. There may still be some natural secrets, some wonderful creatures surviving.

With this in mind we celebrate the wonder of creation, the animals, plants, birds and fish, which make our globe a truly wonderful place. As humans we have care of the planet, may we treasure it.

These are our thoughts and this is our prayer.

An illustration for this story is to be found on ***page154.***

Patrick

Many years ago in a small village near the sea, a young boy named Patrick lived happily with his mother. Each day Patrick would run down to the beach to meet his friends. They would play games on the sand, chase one another and skim stones on the high tide.

Each evening Patrick would sit with his mother in their small cottage, telling stories and singing songs. When it was time for bed, Patrick's mother would say, "Patrick, whatever happens, wherever you go, you must be brave, have courage. Always remember that I love you, even if I'm not with you."

"I know mother," replied Patrick.

"And Patrick," she continued, "don't forget to say your prayers, remember God is with you, always near you." She would then tuck Patrick into bed and he would fall asleep feeling warm and secure.

One blustery Autumn morning Patrick was running on the beach, watching the waves break and listening to the screech of the gliding seagulls. As he looked out to the horizon he caught sight of a ship sailing towards the shore. The ship slowed down and some men lowered themselves down into a large rowing boat. The men were strong and they rowed powerfully through the choppy waters towards the beach.

"Patrick, I think we should go," said one of the children in a slightly worried tone of voice. The men landed and started running towards the children.

"Patrick we should go home, come on quick."

The children broke into a run as they realised that the men were chasing them. Patrick hesitated, surely these men meant no harm. Whilst Patrick was thinking, all the other children had run off. The men were suddenly upon him, they grabbed him and even though he struggled he was bundled into the rowing boat and soon found himself being lifted onto the ship.

Patrick had no idea how long the journey on the ship took. He was tied up in the dark hull of the vessel, feeling terrified and alone. When he was finally brought up to the deck he realised that the ship had docked and cargo was being unloaded at a busy port.

"Come on you," shouted one of the sailors roughly at Patrick. Patrick was led down the gang-plank and through busy, dirty streets into a market place. In one area there were a number of boys the same age as him looking scared and lonely just as he must have done. Patrick was dragged across and tied up with the other boys. The sailors started to call out across the market place.

"Fine strong boys for sale. Suitable for any type of work."

'We're being sold as slaves,' thought Patrick and panic shot through him. Would he ever see his mother again?

"He looks about right," said one man looking and pointing at Patrick. He took hold of Patrick's arms and pulled him, Patrick resisted.

"Good he's strong, I'll take him, how much do you want for him?"

The sailor looked Patrick up and down and said, "Two hundred."

The man agreed and led Patrick away to a horse drawn cart.

"Don't look so scared," said the man, "you'll be fine on my farm, you can take care of my sheep, I'll feed you and give you a shelter. And if you prove yourself I'll give you your freedom." Patrick continued to look and feel more terrified and sad than he ever had in his entire life.

Patrick's new home was a small shepherd's hut high up in the hills in the West of this new country. His job was to watch over the huge flock of sheep that grazed on the hillside. At night he had to be extra vigilant for wolves and wild dogs, who would try to kill sheep for food. When the sheep were all safely closed into their fields for the night, Patrick would sit in his small hut, with a single candle, thinking about his home.

He would often think of his mother and remember how she had spoken to him. Tears would come into Patrick's eyes as he recalled her love for him. But he also knew she still loved him even though she wasn't there. He had not forgotten that his mother had told him that God was always with him, beside him, in front of him, always near. He said his prayers and asked God to look after him. So although Patrick was lonely, he didn't feel alone, he had his mother's love and God with him.

Patrick worked hard on the hillside, tending the sheep and for many years took great care of the gentle animals. Often in winter he would tramp through deep snow to the highest reaches of the hill to find one lost sheep. The farmer appreciated Patrick's work and recognized that Patrick worked hard.

One Spring morning the farmer came up the hillside to Patrick's hut and said, "Patrick you have served me and my sheep well for many a long year. Now you should be free. I don't know where you are from but it's time to return to your real home."

Patrick's heart leapt with joy. He gathered together his things and set out down the hill towards the port.

When he reached the port he met a great many people. He noticed how most people looked poor and sad. He could tell that some of these people were afraid and alone. 'These people need help, my help,' he thought. With that in mind he climbed on board a ship heading for his old home.

Patrick would never forget the look on his mother's face when he ran up to their cottage. "Patrick, Patrick, I don't believe it, you've come home," she cried and threw her arms tightly around him.

Patrick sat with his mother in front of the fire that night and told her all about what had happened to him. About how he was terrified and alone and how the thought of her love and the closeness of God had kept him going.

"Mother, there are many sad and lonely people in that country across the sea, they need help. I want to go back and help them," he said as he looked into her eyes.

"I don't believe it," she cried.

Patrick didn't know what to say. Tears ran on her cheeks and then she continued. "I can hardly believe you could have so much courage. After all you've been through, you have the strength to think of other people who need your help. That is true courage," she said with pride.

And so it was that Patrick sailed again to the country across the sea. Not as a slave, but as a young man setting out to do good and help other people.

Thought/Prayer

God of the World,

May we have the courage that we need to face the challenges of life. May we be strong and true and always remember those who love and support us.

We think especially of all of the people who have lost their strength and determination because of conflict and poverty.

May they find strength and courage to look for a brighter future.

These are our thoughts and this is our prayer.

Zom and Zorg Visit Planet Earth

Theme: The Need for Conservation

Introduction:
Two alien explorers visit The Earth. They see that it is a beautiful planet, but when they visit again some things have changed.

"This is a most beautiful place," said Zorg.

The two aliens stood together on a gently sloping hill looking across a wide plain. Majestic elephants moved in herds, their tusks glinting in the sunlight. Elegant eagles glided effortlessly above the scene, whilst tiny colourful birds flitted in and out of the nearby trees. The air was sweet and clear and the intoxicating scent of thousands of fragile flowers filled the atmosphere.

"Indeed this planet is more lovely than our own," continued Zom, "what is this planet called?"

"This is Earth, a small but very full planet with a wide variety of life and natural resources."

The two aliens were on a mission, travelling to the farthest corners of the universe to find out all they could about other planets. They had landed on earth ten thousand years ago, when it was in its raw state. There were no buildings, no roads, factories or shops.

The two space travellers set out across the land looking at the variety of wildlife, the flowers, trees, insects and animals. Eventually they reached a surging river. They marvelled at the salmon jumping the rocks as they travelled upstream to spawn. Otters played amongst the thick reeds. The water was clear and fresh. The alien friends looked at one another and smiled.

"When we go home we can report that this planet Earth is the most wonderful place in the solar system," said Zorg enthusiastically. Zom suddenly dropped to the ground.

"Get down, quick," he whispered to his friend.

"What is it?" breathed Zorg as he dropped into the undergrowth. But as he looked up he realised why they had hidden themselves. On the other bank of the river a man dressed in animal skins was creeping towards a large goose. The man held a spear made roughly from a branch, tipped with a flint knife.

"Is that a human?" asked Zorg.

"I think so, we'd better leave. This planet is in the care of humans, it wouldn't do for us to be seen."

The aliens found their way back to their spacecraft and launched up into the sky.

"I do hope those humans look after this wondrous place," remarked Zorg as he watched Planet Earth grow smaller.

Several thousand years later, on a distant planet, Zorg and Zom, two old alien friends sat together recalling their travels across the universe when they were young alien explorers.

"Zorg, do you remember that Planet Earth?" asked Zom eagerly.

"Oh most certainly," replied Zorg, "what a fantastic planet that was. All of those amazing animals and plants. The sweet smelling air and the clear, fresh water. I have often dreamt about the beauty of that place."

"You know Zorg, I would love to make one more space journey and visit Earth again," enthused Zom.

An excited sparkle came into Zorg's eyes.

"Oh that would be wonderful," he replied, "but it's been a long time since we were there, I wonder if it has changed very much?"

It wasn't long before their spacecraft was bursting through the Earth's atmosphere and touching down in a cloud of smoke and steam.

The space travellers looked around as they walked down the ramp from the ship.

"I thought we were meant to land in a forest, there are no trees here?" questioned Zorg.

"I know, this place was thick with woodland when we were last here, it looks as though they've been cut down," exclaimed Zom. The scene was bleak, thousands of burnt tree stumps, no signs of the birds, insects and animals that had once lived there. "What's happened? Let's go down to the river," said Zom.

The aliens approached the river. Where there had once been open fields leading down to the flowing water, there were several large factories and power plants. Dark smoke was rising from tall chimneys and an acrid smell hung in the air. The river water moved slowly, heavy with thick oil and waste pumped from the factories. Some fish floated lifeless on the surface. Zorg and Zom stood motionless gazing at the polluted water.

"What has happened?" asked Zom. "Why has this planet been spoilt?"

They decided to fly to another part of the world.

They landed on an African plain just in time to witness some poachers chasing a large elephant for its ivory tusks. "We must stop them!" shouted Zom.

"No!" declared Zorg, "we are not allowed to interfere, these humans have been given this planet, it is up to them to use it as they want."

"But we can't allow them to destroy all this beauty, to waste all of these natural resources," exclaimed Zom.

"This planet is in the hands of the humans, they must decide," replied Zorg.

The space travellers returned to their craft. They were sad and disappointed. They looked down and saw the thousands of cars and lorries pumping out exhaust fumes. They watched as the brutal wood merchants cut down the precious rainforest. They sighed as they realised that some species of animals were lost forever.

"Can this planet be saved and reborn?" asked Zom.

"Yes, if the humans choose to, they could work together to look after the planet, cut down on pollution, recycle materials and find alternative forms of power."

"But will they do these things?" asked Zom.

"I just don't know," replied Zorg.

Their spacecraft swung away from the Earth, a bright light was visible twinkling like a question in the sky. It moved quickly into the depths of the galaxy and disappeared.

Thought/Prayer

God of the World,

Our planet faces many threats to its natural resources because of the actions of mankind.

May communities work together to take measures, which conserve the Earth's beauty and natural habitats.

These are our thoughts and this is our prayer.

An illustration for this story is to be found on page 155.

Jacob's Story

Theme: Easter Week

Introduction:
Jacob witnesses some of the events of holy week.
This story was written by Jacob. It is his account of what happened during an amazing week when he was a young man in Jerusalem.

My arms started to ache, I could feel the pull in my shoulder as I lifted the palm branch aloft once more. I did this everytime someone shouted, 'He is here.' A cheer would go up and the palms were thrust high above our heads. We had been told he was coming travelling on a donkey and we would see him soon.

I was nervous with anticipation. My stomach felt fuzzy. I had seen him once before and looked into his deep brown eyes. I'd felt the power of his words change my life. I couldn't wait to see him again. Everyone in the crowd must have felt the same for there were a great number of us. All ready with our palm branches ready to hail the King.

At the edge of the crowd some Roman soldiers shuffled from foot to foot. They were not entirely sure what was going on.

All at once the volume of the throng rose. The hum of voices became a crescendo of cheers and there coming over the brim of the hill I saw him.

His white robe was pulled up off the ground so that it didn't get caught up in the donkey's feet. His brown hair blew in the wind and the warm smile spread across his dusty face. "Hosanna, Hosanna for the King!" we chanted.

The pain in my arm was gone. I flapped my palm branch with more gusto than ever. I felt like I had taken off. I was high on praise as he, Jesus, rode past within a few metres, waving.

The following Thursday evening I sat with my brothers in Gethsemane. We were flicking olive stones and chatting. My oldest brother Joshua was telling us how he'd seen Jesus several times during that week. He declared that he was worried because the High Priests and the Romans were on edge with the amount of adoration that Jesus was receiving. Josh said that the authorities felt threatened.

As the sun began to sink and the rays spilt out over the olive trees in the garden, a group of men came into the glade. Some of them were a bit loud, they'd obviously had too much wine.

Suddenly I caught my breath for there amongst the men was Jesus.

I signalled my brothers and we moved forward slowly to get a better view. Jesus and his group of friends did not see us. We sat still and watched.

But where was that generous smile that Jesus wore last Sunday? Where were the stars in his eyes? He looked sad. He appeared frail and smaller than before.

One by one his friends slumped down on the grass. He moved amongst them speaking quietly. I couldn't tell what he was saying but his body language displayed disappointment.

Jesus moved away from the group and walked towards a rising rock formation. He scaled the rocks easily and then sat gazing up at the sky.

The faint suggestion of the sun still hung orange in the atmosphere. A cooler breeze blew across the garden.

The saviour stood up, his figure silhouetted against the semi light. He raised his arms and threw back his head and let out a cry. The sound was powerful, it was also sad and scared all at once.

The darkness dropped and I didn't see where Jesus went. The next I knew my brother was shaking me urgently.

"Quick," he called, "soldiers are coming into the garden."

I spied a group of soldiers striding purposefully across the grass towards Jesus and his followers. In amongst the soldiers was a man that I recognised. I had seen him earlier in the week with Jesus. I couldn't understand why he was with Roman soldiers.

The man approached Jesus and kissed him. I noticed that he didn't look Jesus in the eye, he simply hung his head.

At that moment there was a violent commotion. The soldiers rushed forward and grabbed Jesus. Jesus' men roused themselves and began to fight with the soldiers.

Joshua grabbed me and bundled me out of the garden. I didn't see what happened to Jesus.

It was later the next afternoon that I found out what had become of Jesus. I had been drawn to the noise of the crowd, which was gathered to watch a crucifixion. I peered over the heads of the throng and I choked and felt dizzy. It was Jesus.

His body was bent with pain under the weight of the cross. Slowly he stepped up onto the rising ground. Each step appeared a torment.

As he passed me he looked up and I caught his glimpse. His eyes, though full of agony, still had their depth and warmth.

"Jesus!" I called out and reached out my hand. The crowd surged forward and my reach was blocked.

I turned away and sat down on the ground. Tears welled up in my eyes. I couldn't bear to go any further.

Thought/Prayer

God of the World,

At Easter time we think about the suffering of Jesus and the important message he brought for the world.

May we take the Easter message of new life and examine the way we live our lives.

These are our thoughts and this is our prayer.

Theme: Nature Conservation

Introduction:
David loves to visit Wales to stay with his grandparents. One particular Summer he shares his natural discovery with his grandfather.

"No David, I'm not going to the beach again today, I'm fed up with the beach."
Ged shouted and then turned away to continue playing games on his mobile phone. David disappointedly looked out the windows at the fields above the house.

Every year the two brothers came to Wales to stay with their granny and grandad. Most years they spent nearly all of the time on the beach, rain or shine. But Ged was now a teenager and his interest in the sea and the sand had waned. Ged was now devoted to his teenage mates, the charts and his mobile phone, he was no longer prepared to spend hours searching the rock pools or splashing in the waves.

David wandered through to see his Grandad hoping for some activity.

"Grandad would you like to go for a walk down to the beach?" asked David eagerly. He was hoping for an ice cream.

David's Grandfather looked at him over his glasses and said, "Well Davey, I don't fancy the beach but I'll take you to the river in Cooper's Valley if you like?"

'No ice cream shops there,' thought David but he was pleased to get some attention.

When they reached the top of the valley they felt the wind in the back of their throats as it whipped across the hillside. They descended into the valley and came closer to the river. David suddenly grabbed his grandad's sleeve.

"Look Grandad," he hissed, "a bird, I think it's a duck near the bank."

"Yes Davey boy, that's a duck, it's about all you'll see on this river nowadays."

They got a little closer to the brown Mallard before it floated away. David was not used to seeing any wildlife other than the pigeons and the occasional rat. He was always delighted to have a wildlife encounter, even if it was just with a very ordinary duck.

"What do you mean Grandad, did you ever see other animals and birds here?" he asked.

"When I was a young man Davey, I would walk along this river bank early in the morning and sometimes spy a family of otters splashing in the shallow parts of the river. It was the most wonderful vision." Grandad's eyes were alight with the special memory. "But of course," he continued with disdain in his voice, "the processing factory opened, the river was polluted with all that filth and the otters died out, what a crime to destroy God's creatures."

David said nothing but lamented the fact that he could have seen otters once in this river. He looked into the water trying to see evidence of the offending pollution, but the river looked quite clear.

The man and the boy walked on up over the next rise and through some woodland beside the water. Spots of rain found their way through the trees and David could sense that his grandfather was getting cold. Just as they turned to return home, David saw a modern building and a fenced car park up ahead where the land flattened out.

"What's that place Grandad?" he asked eagerly.

"Oh I don't know, some visitors' centre that the council have spent too much money on," replied the old man with a little sarcasm in his voice.

David realised that there was no point asking any more about the building, but he silently decided to return alone another time.

David went straight in at the house and put on the kettle for his grandad's tea. "Thanks for taking me to Cooper's Valley, Grandad, I might go back there another day," David suggested enthusiastically.

"Good lad," his grandfather replied and sat down with his tea in front of the television.

It was four days later when David made his way along the river again. This time he continued to the new building that he had seen. He read the sign,

COOPER'S VALLEY WILDLIFE VISITORS' CENTRE

"Wildlife," thought David with doubt, "all I saw was one duck."

But as he entered the clean, warm building he saw beautiful photographs of trout, herons, water voles all manner of water birds and there at the end of the display - otters. David moved slowly round the display cases admiring the evidence of the beautiful creatures. After a moment the Centre's warden spoke to David.

"Can I help you young man? Would you like to know more about Cooper's Valley wildlife?" he asked gently.

David was a bit confused, but he burst out. "I didn't think there was much wildlife in the river because of the pollution from the processing factory. My grandad said that . . ." David's words faltered.

"Well that used to be true ten years ago," replied the warden, "but then the factory closed, we cleaned up the river, reintroduced some wildlife and the rest just found their way back. In fact," he continued with delight, "there's more wildlife here than before the factory."

David was amazed and thrilled, he then asked the question which was popping around in his brain.

"What about the otters, are there any in the river?"

"Otters, oh yes," the warden confirmed, "but you'll only see them around seven in the evening when it's a bit quieter, they come out to play and feed down by those large rocks."

David followed the warden's hand as he pointed to some rocks between two large willow trees.

David thanked the warden, checked his watch and went home.

'How long had it been since his grandfather had visited the river before they went together yesterday?' David mused.

At six thirty exactly David thanked his granny for his tea and declared that he was going for a walk. His brother Ged looked up from his mobile phone and enquired, "Where are you going Dave?"

"Oh just along the river," he replied casually. But Ged had already lost interest.

David found a quiet spot hidden behind some brambles just above the rocks at the side of the river. He waited anxiously, his eyes scanning the water for signs of life. Another duck and then a coot sailed past. And then with a twitching movement and a flick of whiskers it appeared. A silver grey-brown, sleek otter. The animal sniffed the air turned its head backwards as if to signal to the others who soon tripped out into the shallow water. One obviously had some food in its mouth. David held his breath, not daring to move. This was totally and incredibly exciting. David quivered with the thrill.

He watched for many minutes as the beautiful creatures played and splashed in the river. They chased one another, tumbled together, arguing over food and jumped amongst the reeds.

David had to show his grandad, he knew that he would be amazed. But David said nothing until the next day in the middle of the afternoon.

"Grandad, will you come for another walk with me to Cooper's Valley after tea?" he asked. His grandfather clearly was a little less enthusiastic, but agreed.

David took his grandfather to the secluded place near the rocks. The old man looked a little confused as David made him sit down quietly and peer between the undergrowth.

"Just watch the river Grandad," David hissed.

After a few tense minutes David was rewarded. The otters splashed into view. His grandfather was trembling, but he said nothing he just gently took hold of David's arm and a broad silent smile spread across his face.

They watched the wonderful animals for over twenty minutes, not a word was spoken.

When they finally stood up to go home, Grandad spoke, "Davey that's the most wonderful thing I've seen in years, but . . . " his words faltered to a stop and David could see the small dribble of a tear run down his cheek.

As they walked towards the house David explained everything that the warden had told him. His grandfather had known about the factory closing but had no idea that the river had been cleaned up. He had never dreamed that the otters could return to the river.

From then on Grandad regularly walked in Cooper's Valley. And when David visited in the Summer they would go together and encounter the beautiful otters.

Thought/Prayer

God of the Valleys and Streams,

We are grateful for the wonder of creation. It is fantastic that we can see wildlife all around us.

We give thanks for the organisations which work hard to preserve the habitats of many different animals and plants. May their work continue to help the survival of the more endangered species.

We must try to live in harmony with wildlife and be sure that our actions do not threaten nature.

These are our thoughts and this is our prayer.

An illustration for this story is to be found on page 156.

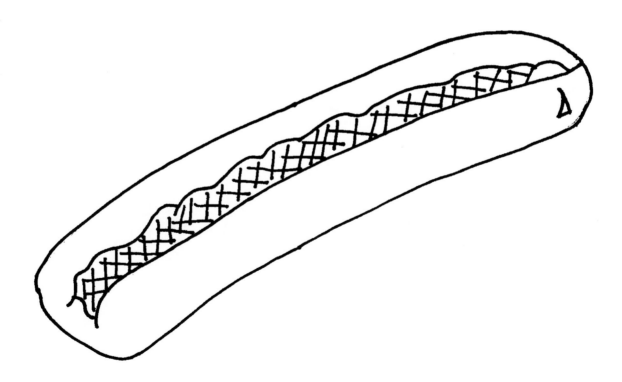

Michael Such and the Cake Shop - Drawing by Ellen

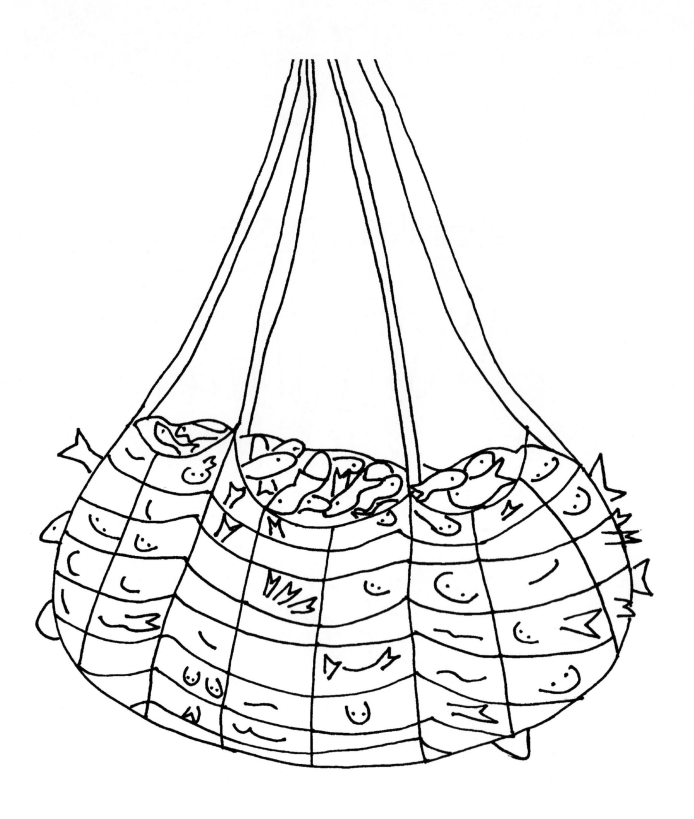

Captain McCullough- Drawing by Ellen

The Dodo- Drawing by Michael

Kasim and Twinkle - Drawing by Fiona

Senat is Determined- Drawing by Ellen

Lucky Cat - Drawing by Michael

Katie was Always in a Rush- Drawing by Fiona

Inderveer the Fisherman - Drawing by Ellen

Messages- Drawing by Michael

143

Ngonda's Walkabout - Drawing by Michael

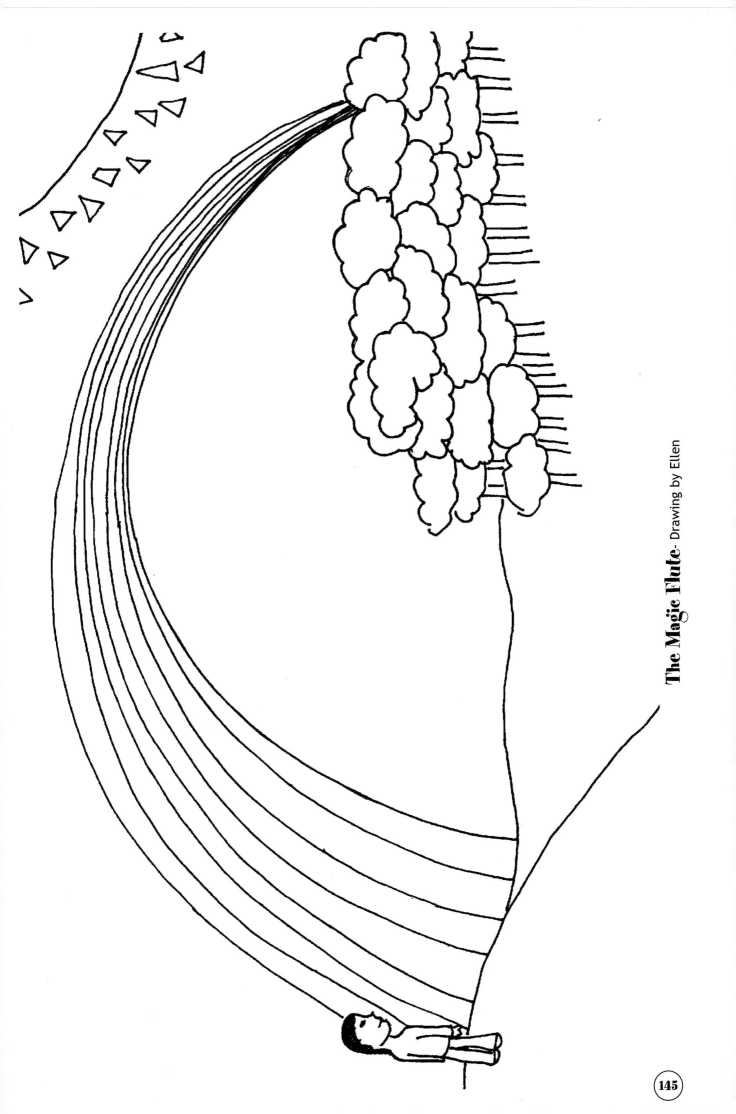

The Magic Flute- Drawing by Ellen

145

Pet Day - Drawing by Ellen

Pat's Cup Final- Drawing by Michael

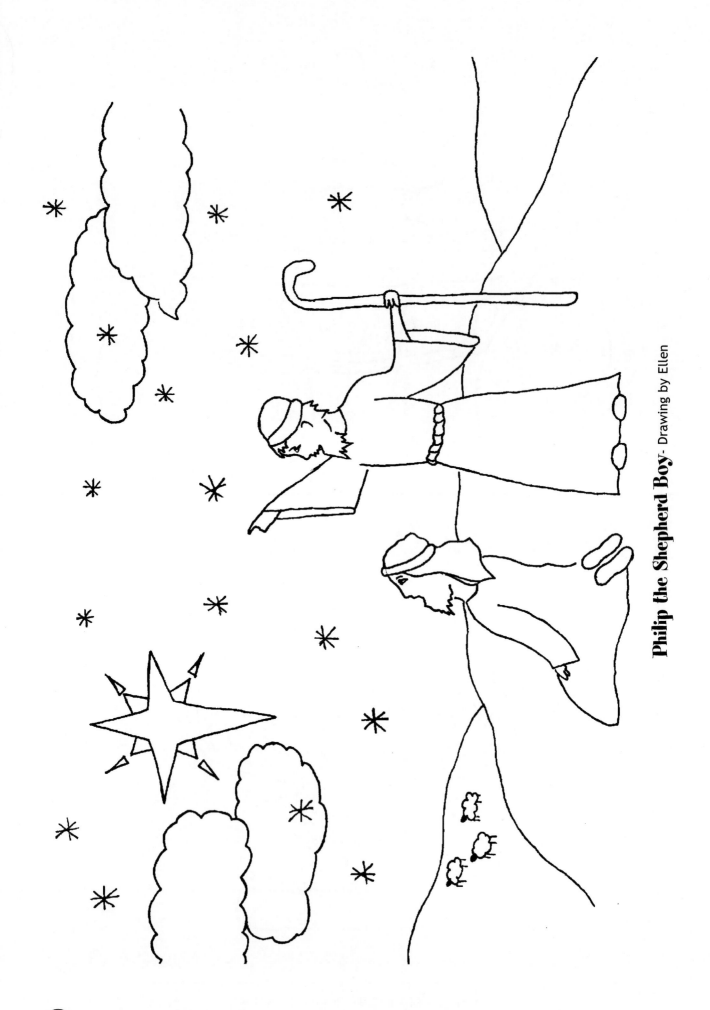

Philip the Shepherd Boy- Drawing by Ellen

Promise- Drawing by Ellen

The Emperor's Lake - Drawing by Ellen

The Mask - Drawing by Ellen

The Peace Dove- Drawing by Ellen

The Mindu Plant - Drawing by Ellen

Under the Sea - Drawing by Michael

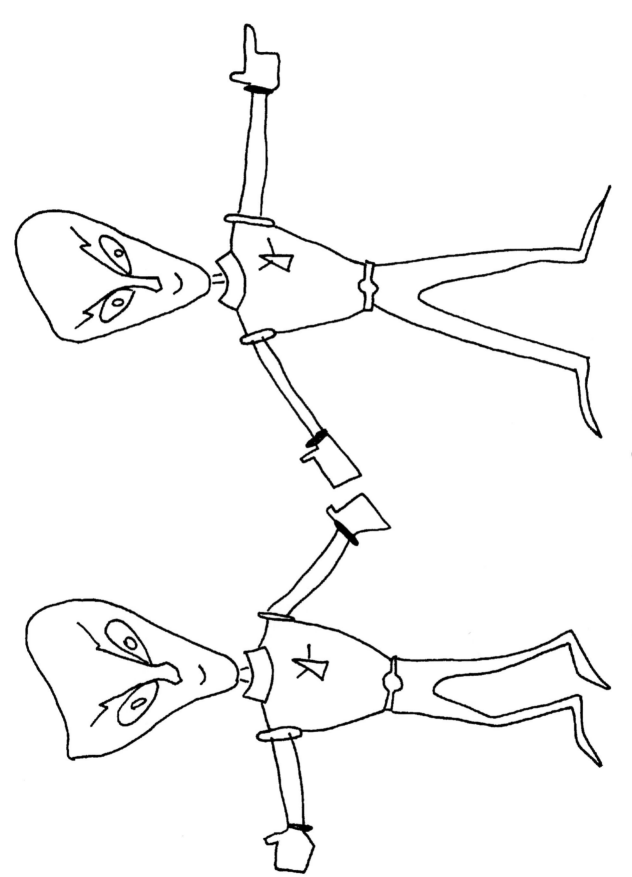

Zom and Zorg Visit Planet Earth - Drawing by Fiona

155

Cooper's Valley - Drawing by Ellen